A ROADMAP FOR SUCCESS

Transforming Advanced Illness Care in America

Library of Congress Cataloging-in-Publication Data:
ISBN 9781633185296
Printed in the United States of America

The Coalition to Transform Advanced Care (C-TAC) is a national non-profit, non-partisan alliance of 100+ patient and consumer advocacy groups, health care professionals and providers, private sector stakeholders, faith-based organizations, and health care payers with the shared vision that *all Americans with advanced illness, especially the sickest and most vulnerable, will receive comprehensive, high-quality person and family-centered care that is consistent with their goals and values and honors their dignity.*

This book is dedicated to family caregivers all over America. You are quiet, courageous heroes who find pride and determination in caring for your loved ones. We are all better because of the care and compassion you demonstrate every day. Thank you.

It is also dedicated to Alice Koutsoumpas, Tom's mother, whose experience living with advanced illness for many years inspired his work to transform advanced illness care; and to Tom's sister, Melinda, her tireless and devoted caregiver, whose experience underscored the need to create and advocate for a new path forward.

And, it is dedicated to Bill's brother-in-law, George Cole, who is in hospice care in Bozeman, Montana as this is written. George has lived an enviable life of family, fun and remarkable creativity in work and play. And, now he is leaving us with grace and courage. He and his wife, Susie, show all of us the way forward.

CONTENTS

FOREWORD

Life is precious. And we want to live it on our own terms. All of it. But when it comes to advanced illness, too often we are swept into uncharted territories for ourselves and our families. We don't understand all the medical jargon. We don't always get all the facts and support we need to make our own decisions. We feel lost.

A Roadmap for Success: Transforming Advanced Illness Care in America: A Blueprint for Reforming Advanced Illness Care in America offers hope for a different way of dealing with the challenges that advanced illness brings to individuals—and to the neighbors, family members and friends who so often serve as family caregivers. It calls for all of us to work together to confront the obstacles that stand in the way of better care and caring. It offers promising practices that demonstrate that we can change the way we view the world of advanced illness and those who find themselves thrust into that mysterious world. It gives us a way to stop seeing people as a set of medical diagnoses and treatments, but instead as whole people with minds, bodies, social connections, and lifelong values that guide them. It gives us hope that we can put patients and families first, and that we can create policies that support these directions.

Like many of you who read this book, I come to this transformative work with many hats. I am a nurse with deep roots in helping people live independently in their homes and communities—especially when illness or disabilities challenge their ability to do so. That work led me to a life-long passion to better understand how to support family caregivers in their crucial work and to create services and public policies that make it possible. Several years ago, I had the great good fortune to join AARP, the 37 million member organization that advocates for these very issues. AARP is a member of the Coalition to Transform Advanced Care (C-TAC), and I serve on the Professional Engagement Workgroup to encourage nurses and other clinicians to engage in effective shared decision-making with patients and their families.

Of course, like most if not all of you, I also have my own personal stories—my mother, my father, my mother-in-law, my nephew, my sister's best friend, and many more. I get the calls as a nurse, daughter, sibling, aunt, neighbor, former policy official…all those hats. These are important people in my life. And their calls for help were so compelling… frightened, confused, and lost in the maze. It's heartbreaking.

People should not have to have a nurse in the family to help them one-on-one. And many clinicians need help themselves to know where to turn for information, tools, and help.

That is why this book is so important. It brings together the thinking of a diverse alliance of experts, advocates, faith-based organizations, policymakers, employers, and other private-sector stakeholders. Health care professionals and providers share new, evidence-based practices that can truly change the typical way we currently experience advanced illness care—fragmented, undignified, uniformed, exhausting. There are examples of health providers that have made changes and are getting it right. They not only inspire us to transform advanced illness care, they show us how. And perhaps more importantly, they show us what a big impact "doing it right" can have on patients, their loved ones and caregivers. Employers also discuss the implications of the dysfunctional current system on the world of work and workers, and how changing that system can not only provide better support for employees, but also benefit employers as well. There are recommendations for policy changes and for metrics that can help us follow our progress. And much more, told from important perspectives, but all leading us toward the path of transformation.

We need to take this path now. The current situation is unacceptable. We want to live on our own terms. We want to know our options. If we have families involved with us, we do not want them to be stressed out by confusing and contradictory information. We want them to have the help they need to support us—and we want them to get attention to their own needs for support. *A Roadmap for Success: Transforming Advanced Illness Care in America* provides a guide for making that happen, but in order to succeed, we must all make that journey together.

I am optimistic. I hope you are as well. Please join in following *A Roadmap for Success: Transforming Advanced Illness Care in America.* For your sake. For your own families. And for mine.

Susan C. Reinhard
Senior Vice President, AARP Public Policy Institute
and Chief Strategist, Center to Champion Nursing in America

ACKNOWLEDGEMENTS

Just as it takes the hard work and dedication of many talented people to transform advanced illness care in America, it has taken many hardworking, dedicated and talented people to make this book possible. While we can't mention all of them, we would like to recognize a few.

We begin by thanking the expert authors who contributed their expertise and insights into writing the chapters of the book (see About the Contributors). These are nationally recognized experts who are not only deeply immersed in the issues surrounding advanced illness care, but they are care intensely about improving advanced care in this country. The mere fact that they would take the time away from their everyday work to contribute to this book is evidence of their dedication and commitment to the cause.

This book would not have possible without our sponsors, AARP and the American Hospital Association (AHA). We not only thank Susan Reinhard, Senior Vice President of AARP and Chief Strategist at the Center to Champion Nursing in America, and Rich Umbdenstock, CEO of the American Hospital Association for contributing the Foreword and the Introduction, we also thank the members of the AARP and AHA staffs who contributed in various ways. This includes from AARP: Kevin Donnellan, AARP Chief of Staff; Debra Whitman, Executive Vice President, Policy, Strategy and International Affairs; Jodi Lipson, AARP's Book Division Director, who oversaw the publication of the book; and Elizabeth Costle, Lina Walker and Jordan Green from AARP's Public Policy Institute; Rhonda Richards from AARP's State and National Group; and Dorothy Siemon from AARP's Office of Policy Integration who offered expert insights into the various aspects of advanced illness care. And from AHA, we also thank Becky Meadows and Ashley Thompson.

We owe a deep debt of gratitude to the C-TAC board of directors for their support of this project (many contributed chapters as well) and to the C-TAC staff who worked above and beyond the call of duty to help make this book happen. We especially thank David Longnecker, M.D., C-TAC's clinical innovations officer, for his leadership and his contribution on metrics; Jon Broyles, executive director, for his tireless work in spearheading this project; and Meagan Johnston, C-TAC's communications director, for leading the communications efforts around the book. We also thank C-TAC staff members Raca Banerjee for her work on Chapter 6, Purva Rawal, Kevin Kappel, Jackie Buente and Sasha Simpson, for their guidance, insights, suggestions and editorial review.

Many other people contributed their knowledge, insights and expertise to the writing of this book through their quotes, personal stories and experiences, and we thank all of them, especially Jay Mahoney, principal of the Summit Business Group, LLC; Jack Watters, M.D., Vice President for External Medical Affairs at Pfizer; Suzanne Johnson, MPH, RN, Vice President, Sharp Hospice Care; and Khue Nguyen, co-founder and Chief Operating Officer of ACIStrategies. We also give a special thanks to Deborah Kent, who created the cover and designed the book.

Finally, we would like to thank all of those pioneers including "Hospice Heros" who have blazed the trail for the path forward. Without their determination to find a better way, we would not be where we are today. They paved the way out of the advanced care wilderness and made life better for all people needing advanced care and their loved ones. They made A Roadmap for Success: Transforming Advanced Illness Care in America possible, and it is our hope that, thanks to all of the people who poured their heart and soul into this project, this book provides a guide for transforming advanced illness care in America that leads us all to a brighter and better future.

ABOUT THE EDITORS

Tom Koutsoumpas is Co-Chair of The Coalition to Transform Advanced Care (C-TAC) and President and CEO of the National Partnership for Hospice Innovation. Tom has long been recognized as one of the nation's leading experts and advocates for hospice, end-of-life care, advanced illness, and Medicare-eligible populations. With a career that spans work from the U.S. Senate and the Indiana Governor's Office to one of the nation's oldest and largest hospice providers and also one of the nation's largest health care companies working in both policy and operations, Tom has worked to ensure that federal and state health care programs provide ready access to quality, compassionate, and cost-effective care for those who are facing a life-limiting illness. He was instrumental in the development of the Medicare Hospice Benefit and received the Founder's Award from the National Hospice and Palliative Care Organization (NHPCO) in 2008 in recognition of his extraordinary skill, passion, and dedication towards expanding quality end-of-life care. In 2012, Capital Caring presented Tom with its Distinguished Advocacy Partner award in recognition for his years of service to improve hospice care in the Washington Metro area. Tom currently serves as Chairman of the Board of Capital Caring, Board Member and former past Board Chair of the National Coalition for Cancer Survivorship (NCCS), former Board Member of the National Center for Medical-Legal Partnership (MLP), former Board Member of the National Hospice Foundation, and former member of the Board of Regents of Georgetown University. Tom co-authored the foreword to the publication, *Having Your Own Say: Getting the Right Care When It Matters Most*, published in 2012 by Gundersen Health System and the Center for Health Transformation.

Bill Novelli is a founder and Co-Chair of The Coalition to Transform Advanced Care (C-TAC), a Distinguished Professor at the McDonough School of Business at Georgetown University, and former CEO of AARP, a membership organization of nearly 38 million people 50 and older. At Georgetown, he teaches in the MBA program and has created and leads the Global Social Enterprise Initiative. Prior to AARP, Bill was President of the Campaign for Tobacco-Free Kids, where he now serves as chairman of the board. Previously, he was Executive Vice President of CARE, the private relief and development organization, and he co-founded and was President of Porter Novelli, now one of the world's largest public relations agencies and part of the Omnicom Group, an international marketing communications corporation. He has written numerous articles and chapters on marketing management, marketing communications, and social marketing in journals, periodicals and textbooks, as well as two books: *Fifty Plus: Give Meaning and Purpose to the Best Time of Your Life* (with Boe Workman, updated 2008) and *Managing the Older Worker* (with Peter Capelli, 2010). Bill serves on a number of boards and committees, including: Healthways, Strategic Partnerships, Campaign for Tobacco-Free Kids, Bipartisan Policy Center Action Network, KaBoom!, the Association of American Medical Colleges, the Institute of Medicine's (IOM) Committee on Transforming End-of-Life Care (which issued the report, *Dying in America: Improving Quality and Honoring Individual Preferences Near the End of Life*) and IOM's Roundtable on Value & Science-Driven Health Care.

Randall (Boe) Workman, Ph.D., has been writing and speaking on aging issues for more than 25 years. As the Director of CEO Communications at AARP he serves as the chief speechwriter for AARP CEO, Jo Ann Jenkins. He is co-author with Bill Novelli of *Fifty Plus: Give Meaning and Purpose to the Best Time of Your Life*, and editor of *Voice of an Aging Nation: Selected Speeches of Horace B. Deets, Voice of Social Change: Selected Speeches of Bill Novelli*, and *Voice of America's Second Aging Revolution: Selected Speeches of A. Barry Rand*. He received his Ph.D. from Indiana University.

ABOUT THE CONTRIBUTORS

Rabbi Richard F. Address, D. Min, serves as Senior Rabbi of Congregation M'kor Shalom in Cherry Hill. N.J. He is the Founder and Director of www. jewishsacredaging.com. He has served congregations and for thirty-three years served on staff of the Union for Reform Judaism. In that capacity, as Founder and Director of the Department of Jewish Family Concerns, he became involved in issues of aging, the impact of technology on end-of-life issues and the spiritual challenges associated with end of life concerns. Rabbi Address speaks and teaches workshops on subjects related to the spirituality of aging and also teaches at the Hebrew Union College-Jewish Institute of Religion in areas associated with family concerns and hosts a weekly radio show in Philadelphia called Boomer Generation Radio. He serves as co-chair of C-TAC's Committee on Spirituality and Diversity.

Nancy Brown has been Chief Executive Officer of the American Heart Association (AHA) since 2009. The AHA is the world's largest voluntary organization dedicated to fighting cardiovascular diseases and stroke globally. She served as co-chairman of the C-TAC Steering Committee and is a leader in reframing how to provide end-of-life care that both respects patient's wishes and ensures quality decision-making and outcomes for families and health care providers. Both because of her work with the AHA and her own personal experiences, Nancy is a passionate supporter of innovative solutions that will serve as a catalyst for systematic changes to care models for patients and their families. Nancy also serves as chairman of the National Health Council and as a board member for a number of health organizations. She has been with the AHA since 1986.

Bernard (Bud) Hammes, Ph.D., is the director of Medical Humanities and Respecting Choices® for Gundersen Health System headquartered in La Crosse, WI, where he provides educational programs for house staff, medical students, nursing students and physician assistant students and provides workshops for the medical staff, nursing staff, social workers and the pastoral care department. Dr. Hammes chairs both the Institutional Review Board and Ethics Committee at Gundersen, and serves the role of ethics consultant on the Ethics Committee. His work has been primarily focused on improving care at the end-of-life with a special focus on advance care planning. This work has resulted in two nationally recognized programs on advance care planning: *If I Only Knew...* and *Respecting Choices*. He served as editor for the 2012 book, *Having Your Own Say: Getting the Right Care When It Matters Most*, and he has authored or co-authored 42 articles and book chapters that focus on clinical ethics, advance care planning and end-of-life issues. He is on the board of directors of C-TAC and serves as the vice president of the International Society of Advance Care Planning. He is also a professor of Clinical Science at the University of Wisconsin-La Crosse, an associate adjunct professor of the Institute for Health and Society at the Medical College of Wisconsin and a clinical assistant professor in the Department of Pediatrics at the University of Wisconsin School of Medicine and Public Health. He also served as the chair of the National POLST Paradigm Task Force. Dr. Hammes was educated at the University of Notre Dame, receiving his bachelor of arts in 1972 and his doctorate in philosophy in 1978. He has taught at the University of Gonzaga in Spokane, WA, and at the University of Wisconsin-La Crosse.

Jennie Chin Hansen, RN, MS, FAAN is CEO of the American Geriatrics Society whose members focus on the health and health care of older adults, especially those who live and manage complex medical, functional and cognitive issues. Prior to AGS, she was president of AARP during the core of health reform. She also served nearly 25 years with On Lok, Inc., a nonprofit family of organizations providing integrated, globally financed and comprehensive, interdisciplinary medical and community-based services for frail and dual eligible older people in San Francisco. On Lok's groundbreaking global payment, integrated and coordinated service delivery became the 1997 federal law that incorporated the Program of All Inclusive Care to the Elderly (PACE) into the Medicare and Medicaid programs, now operating in 30 states. In 2011, she completed a six-year term of the Medicare Payment Advisory Commission (MedPAC). She currently serves as a board member of the SCAN Foundation and the Institute for Healthcare Improvement and was formerly co-chair of the C-TAC Steering Committee.

Pamela Kalen, joined the National Business Group on Health as a Vice President Membership and Member Services in January 2002. She was staff leader to the Business Group's Palliative Care and End-of-Life Work Group, which developed tools for improving awareness of palliative care and end-of-life care as part of the overall health, wellness and plan design strategy for employees. In 2011, she served on the National Quality Forum Palliative Care and End-of-Life Care Endorsement Maintenance Steering Committee which evaluated measures for endorsement as voluntary consensus standards and identified gaps in performance measures. She is a member of C-TAC's Employer Committee as well as a member of the Program Advisory Board for Vital Decisions, an organization that provides counseling to patients and families dealing with advanced illness. Prior to joining the Business Group, she held leadership roles with the Employers' Managed Health Care Association (MHCA) and the Group Health Association of America (AHIP). She received her Master of Business Administration degree and Bachelor of Arts degree from the University of Maryland.

Randall S. Krakauer, MD, is National Medical Director of Medicare, AETNA, Inc., where he is responsible for medical management planning and implementation nationally for Aetna Medicare members, including program development and administration. He has more than 30 years of experience in medicine and medical management, has held senior medical management positions in several major organizations, and currently serves as a Board Member of C-TAC. He is a fellow of the American College of Physicians and the American College of Rheumatology and Professor of Medicine at Seton Hall University Graduate School of Medicine He is also past chairman of the American College of Managed Care Medicine. Dr. Krakauer graduated from Albany Medical College in 1972 and is Board Certified in Internal Medicine and Rheumatology. He received training in Internal Medicine at the University of Minnesota Hospitals and in Rheumatology at the National Institutes of Health and Massachusetts General Hospital/Harvard Medical School, and received an MBA from Rutgers.

Jay Mahoney, is the founder and Principal of the Summit Business Group, LLC, which provides consulting services to hospices, health systems, home health agencies, trade groups, insurance and pharmaceutical companies across the country. He also established the Hospice Compliance Network, a national network of hospices and their corporate compliance officers focused on regulatory and corporate compliance issues for hospices. He began his hospice career as Executive Director of Boulder County Hospice in 1982, and emerged as a state and national leader in the then nascent hospice movement. Boulder County Hospice became one of the first hospices in the country to become a Medicare certified hospice provider and to have its own general inpatient care unit. In 1984, he became head of the National Hospice Organization (NHO) now called the National Hospice and Palliative Care Organization (NHPCO), a position he held for more than 14 years. He has lectured and written extensively on hospice care nationally and around the world. He has received the *Founders Award* from the National Hospice Foundation, the *Inspector General's Integrity Award* from the HHS Office of the Inspector General, the *Administrator's Achievement Award,* from the (now) Centers for Medicare and Medicaid Services and an *Honorary Doctorate* from the University of Colorado. He received his Bachelor and Master degrees from the University of Colorado.

Brent Pawlecki, MD, MMM, is the Chief Health Officer at The Goodyear Tire & Rubber Co., a position he has held since 2011. His responsibilities include global health strategy, providing leadership for Goodyear's medical clinics, fitness facilities, health benefits, health improvement and wellness programs, Employee Assistance Programs, and health related emergencies. Prior to joining Goodyear, he was the Corporate Medical Director at Pitney Bowes, overseeing all health-related issues for the organization, including the Pitney Bowes' award-winning corporate clinics, wellness programs and absence management department, and served as the Chief HIPAA Privacy Officer. During his career, he has worked in a private medical practice as well as the Emergency Department. He attended college and medical school at St. Louis University and completed a combined residency in Internal Medicine and Pediatrics from Bridgeport Hospital and Yale University. He also completed the Master of Medical Management Business Degree from the University of Southern California.

Rev. Tyrone Pitts, General Secretary Emeritus, Progressive National Baptist Convention, is an ordained minister in the Progressive National Baptist Convention, Inc. Prior to joining the National Baptist Convention, Rev. Dr. Pitts was the Director for Racial Justice, Division of Church and Society, National Council of the Churches of Christ in the USA (NCC), where he worked with NCC member communions, the World Council of Churches, the All African Conference of Churches, other ecumenical agencies and community groups to combat racism in the US and throughout the world. He has also served as Past Chairperson of the Baptist Joint Committee on Public Affairs; Member of the Executive Coordinating Committee, General Board and the National Mission Unit of the National Council of the Churches of Christ in the USA (NCC); the Executive Board and Committee of the Baptist World Alliance; Board Member of Baptists Today Newspaper; Vice Chairperson of the Higher Horizon Day Care Center, Bailey's Crossroads, Virginia; former Board member, Southern Christian Leadership Conference West; former member of the Board of Directors, Los Angeles Hospital and Prison Ministry; former chairperson of the Board of Directors of the Bailey's Cross Roads Community Center. Rev. Dr. Pitts has written extensively on racism for national and international publications. He co-chairs C-TAC's Committee on Spirituality and Diversity.

Susan Reinhard, PhD, RN, FAAN, is Senior Vice President of AARP where she directs its Public Policy Institute, the focal point for state, federal and international policy research. She also serves as Chief Strategist for the Center to Champion Nursing in America. Susan is a nationally recognized expert in health and long-term care and family caregiving, with extensive experience in conducting, directing and translating research to promote policy change. Previously, she served as Co-Director of the Rutgers Center for State Health Policy, directing national initiatives to help people with disabilities live at home. She served three governors as Deputy Commissioner of the NJ Department of Health and Senior Services. Dr. Reinhard is a former faculty member at the Rutgers College of Nursing and is a fellow in the American Academy of Nursing. She holds a master's degree in nursing from the University of Cincinnati, and a PhD in Sociology from Rutgers, The State University of New Jersey.

Charles P. Sabatino, is the Director of the American Bar Association's Commission on Law and Aging, where since 1984, he has been responsible for the ABA Commission's research, project development, consultation, and education in areas of health law, longterm care, guardianship and capacity issues, surrogate decisionmaking, legal services delivery for the elderly, and professional ethics. He has written and spoken extensively on capacity issues, advance care planning, surrogate decision-making, and health care policy. He is a member of the board of C-TAC and serves as a legal advisor to the National POLST Paradigm Task Force. Mr. Sabatino is also a Fellow and former president of the National Academy of Elder Law Attorneys and an adjunct professor at Georgetown University Law Center where he teaches Law and Aging. He received his J.D. from Georgetown University Law Center and is a member of the Virginia and D.C. bars.

Mark Schoeberl, MPA, is Executive Vice President of Advocacy and Health Quality for the American Heart Association, where he is responsible for the Association's public policy efforts including policy research, federal and state legislative and regulatory affairs, and community advocacy. He also leads the AHA's health care systems and clinical quality improvement initiatives, including the organization's flagship *Get with the Guidelines* program to improve in-hospital cardiovascular and stroke care. In addition to co-chairing C-TAC's Policy Workgroup, Mark is chair of the board for the Campaign to End Obesity (Washington, DC) and past chair of the National Forum to Prevent Heart Disease and Stroke (Atlanta). Prior to joining the American Heart Association in 2002, he served as deputy and executive staff director for the Iowa Department of Public Health.

Brad Stuart, MD, is co-founder and Chief Executive Officer of Advanced Care Innovation (ACI) Strategies. With more than 35 years of experience practicing internal medicine, palliative care and hospice, and as a health care innovator with a national reputation, he has a career-long commitment to improving clinical and economic outcomes by promoting dignity, choice and responsibility. He created the first Advanced Illness Management (AIM) program in the US with a grant from the Robert Wood Johnson Foundation in 1999, and drove its growth and development toward a national model now adopted by the American Hospital Association and many US health systems and championed by C-TAC, where he served as a founding Board member. For over 10 years Brad has focused on delivery system redesign, specializing in outcome and financial metrics and analytics, physician and staff training, and value-driven cost reduction in advanced illness. A graduate of Stanford University School of Medicine, he was named to the 2013 Health Leaders' Media list of Top 20 national difference-makers and was profiled in *Atlantic Monthly*. He has been named Physician of the Year by the California Association of Health Services at Home. Brad speaks internationally on clinical, economic and spiritual issues in advanced illness.

Nancy Taylor is the Vice President for Public Policy, External Relations, and Communications for The Permanente Federation, Kaiser Permanente's national organization representing the Permanente Medical Groups, and the 17,000 physicians caring for over 9 million Kaiser Permanente members. Nancy oversees the Federation's policy, government relations, marketing, and communications activities of The Permanente Federation, and serves as a liaison between the branding, and communications activities. Nancy is also the Executive Director of the Council of Accountable Physician Practices (CAPP), a consortium of 33 of the nation's most prominent physician-led multi-specialty group practices. In that role, she sets strategy and directs the activities of a non-profit organization working to foster the development and recognition of accountable physician practices as a model for transforming the American health care system. Nancy received her undergraduate degree in Human Biology from Stanford University and her MBA from the Yale School of Management. More recently, she completed the Kaiser Permanente Executive Leadership Program at the Kenan-Flagler School of Business at the University of North Carolina, as well as the Fellows Program at the International Federation of Health Plans.

Rich Umbdenstock is President and Chief Executive Officer of the American Hospital Association (AHA) where he leads, represents and serves more than 5,000 member hospitals, health systems and other health care organizations, and 43,000 individual members. He is also Vice Chair of the National Quality Forum, serves on the Board of Enroll America, and co-chairs the CAQH Provider Council. He also serves on the National Priorities Partnership and was formerly on the C-TAC Steering Committee. His career includes experience in hospital administration; health system governance, management and integration; association governance and management; HMO governance; and health care governance consulting. He has written several books and articles for the health care board audience and has authored national survey reports for AHA, HRET and ACHE. He received a B.A. degree in Politics from Fairfield University (CT), and a master's in Health Services Administration from SUNY- Stony Brook. He is a Fellow of ACHE.

INTRODUCTION

Thanksgiving was Claude's favorite holiday, a day when his favorite people gathered around a table laden with his favorite foods and gave thanks for health and happiness. After dinner, a happy Claude retreated to his favorite armchair and closed his eyes for a little nap. He never awakened.

Many of us hope to die much like Claude did – after a long life in reasonably good health, in our own home, surrounded by loved ones. But can we plan on it?

More often, death is the last stop of a longer journey. Many patients have several chronic conditions that point toward an irreversible decline. Over time, treatment doesn't help much, if at all — and activity, independence and the quality of life begin to decline. Patients may become depressed; the family members caring for them become stressed. And, precious health care dollars are spent providing care that brings neither healing nor comfort to anyone — care that some patients and their families may not even want.

As a health care executive for many years, I have seen people struggle to make heart-wrenching decisions about what a loved one would want if he or she were still able to express a preference. Yet patients and their families are not always given the chance to discuss their options early in the process or to exercise choice later on.

Now, I lead the nation's largest hospital association and find that there is still much to do — and that hospitals are in a unique position to make advanced illness planning a standard part of the care their interdisciplinary teams deliver. I also know that it is a propitious time for hospitals to partner with others in the community to put patients and families first.

The Coalition to Transform Advanced Care (C-TAC), of which the American Hospital Association is a strong supporter and active member, defines advanced illness as one or more conditions serious enough that general health and functioning decline and treatments begin to lose their impact. Even though the trajectory of advanced illness leads to death, many studies show that well-developed advanced Illness management programs not only improve the patient's quality of life, they also reduce the use of unnecessary clinical treatments and hospital admissions, increase patient and family satisfaction and reduce aggregate spending.

C-TAC plays a critical role as the convener of all those who care about making advanced illness planning the norm in honoring the dignity of patients and families. I look forward to the day when all hospitals and care systems organize and deliver high-quality advanced illness management; when all health care professionals have the knowledge and skills to provide it; and when every patient and family understands the benefits of it and the choices available to them.

I believe that day will come sooner as the result of this book. Through it, readers can gain a good understanding of why advanced illness management matters and where it stands today. And everyone concerned about health care and the end of life — from patients and their families; leaders of the health care, employers, faith and public policy community; to practitioners and academics — can understand and feel empowered to implement the action steps needed to achieve high-quality advanced illness care and management.

As health care moves from a volume-based model to a value-based one, and as the baby boom generation ages, our country has an unprecedented opportunity to transform advanced illness management. This is a critical time. And this book defines a path forward. Written in three parts, Section I provides an assessment of the current state of advanced illness care in America, highlighting the progress that has been made over the years as well as the opportunities and challenges that lie ahead. Section II identifies what needs to be done— the key elements of reform. These include putting patients and families first (Chapter 2), the role of spirituality (Chapter 3), the role of employers (Chapter 4), best practice care delivery models (Chapter 5), and the role of public policy and advocacy (Chapter 6). Section III is the "how to" section of the book. It defines the action steps needed to move forward. It sets priorities for moving forward, including how to identify and measure progress and results (Chapter 7), and issues a strong call to action (Chapter 8).

The simple fact is, that while most of us want to die as Claude did—in our own homes, surrounded by loved ones—only about one in four of us do. *A Roadmap for Success: Transforming Advanced Illness Care in America*, provides us with a blueprint for changing that. Our goal is nothing less than to change the way people die in America, so more of us and our families experience our last days as Claude and his family did. I predict that this book will be recognized as an important resource and essential reference in this important effort for years to come.

Rich Umbdenstock
President and Chief Executive Officer
American Hospital Association

SECTION I

**ADVANCED ILLNESS CARE IN AMERICA:
THE BIG PICTURE**

CHAPTER 1

The Current State of Advanced Illness Care in America
Bill Novelli and Tom Koutsoumpas

*"We are all faced with a series of great opportunities—
brilliantly disguised as insoluble problems."*
—John W. Gardner

John Gardner's observation could easily describe the current state of advanced illness care in America. While most Americans today are living longer and healthier lives than ever before, at some point the great majority will face advanced illness. As Nancy Brown, CEO of the American Heart Association, has pointed out, "Advanced illness is as predictable as anything that may arise in our lives, but when it arrives, we are woefully unprepared."[1]

There's a wistful tale among gerontologists about how everyone should live in good health to a ripe old age, well into their 90's, and then have it end with a quick bullet, fired by a jealous lover. But we all know that's not the way most people in America head off into the great beyond.

What is it that people actually want when they are seriously ill and may be approaching life's end? Research indicates that they want: to be at home, with family and friends; they want to have their pain managed and controlled; they want their spiritual wishes and needs to be respected and honored; and they want to be assured that those who love them are not emotionally and financially devastated in the process.

But all too often, that's not what our health system and our society provide. There is a very large gap between the kind of care and treatment people say they want when the end is near and what our society and health system currently provide. Often those with advanced illness receive aggressive treatment, even when that treatment is inconsistent with patient and family requests and values (sometimes grimly referred to as "assault and battery care"). And even when there is little chance of prolonging a quality life. Studies show that providing this kind of care can actually have the opposite effect of what is intended. And this punishing experience is accompanied by a huge toll on families, to our health care system and to society. Most people want to die at home, but the majority of us die in hospitals, often isolated, in pain, and as noted, at great expense to all concerned.

Americans facing advanced illness want and need seamless, person-centered, coordinated care that helps them live as happily, comfortably and productively as possible. But as noted, few people, especially those who face financial hardship, receive it. While our health care system, in most cases, is technologically capable of delivering such care, for many reasons, many people who are in a state of advanced illness do not receive it. In fact, technology, the great blessing of our age in so many ways, is part of the problem, in that clinicians now have the ability to keep people "alive" almost regardless of what they want or what medical state they are in. While some people may want such aggressive treatment, many do not. The type and level of care provided should be consistent with wishes and values of the person receiving the care and his or her family.

It is certainly true that over the last several decades, our health system has made great strides in caring for people with advanced illness, and therein lies the opportunity. Thanks to the work of dedicated people and committed organizations, we now know much more about advanced illness care, what its components are, what distinguishes it in practice, and the effect that quality advanced illness care can have on patients and their families. Yet, despite this progress, very significant challenges and barriers still remain to making quality advanced illness care available to all who need it.

In this opening chapter, we provide an overview of advanced illness care in America. We will discuss the opportunity we have now with the aging of the baby boom generation to build upon the progress that has already been made as well as the opportunities and challenges that lie ahead. As noted in the Foreword, this book is about making things happen. Our goal is to provide solutions, to win the day, to ensure that all people with advanced illness receive the right care at the right time in the right place and that that care empowers patients and their families and honors their dignity. Achieving this goal will not only benefit patients and their families, but our broader society as well.

As with any complex social and medical arena, there are many definitions, descriptions and meanings to contend with. When we talk about *Advanced illness*, we are referring to a state of life that occurs when one or more conditions become serious enough that general health and functioning decline, curative care is less effective, and palliative care to treat the psychosocial and other needs of the patient is recommended—a process that continues to the end of life. This trajectory can last for some years, or perhaps only a few months.

A number of clinical factors help identify advanced illness, including: one or more serious illnesses that are either at a late stage, progressively debilitating, or that lead to unexpected, multiple emergency hospital visits. The continuum below indicates a progression of life, beginning with healthy people and extends on to those who are hospice eligible.

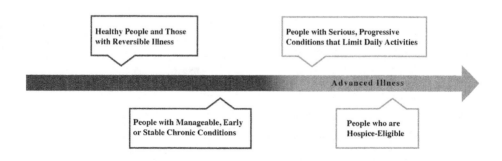

Importantly, the diagram above describes advanced illness on a "health continuum," not an "age continuum." Anyone at any age can develop a need for advanced illness care. It can strike infants and older adults and anyone in between. But to be clear, advanced illness usually occurs among the frail elderly, when one or more chronic conditions—such as cancer, heart disease, or vascular disease—progress to the point where general health and functioning decline, response to treatment diminishes and care needs increase. As we age, more and more people are living with multiple chronic diseases, with the limitations of managing personal care, of where they are able to live and their degree of independence.

It is no secret that America, indeed the entire world, is aging. Over the next two decades, the number of people age 65 and older will nearly double to more than 72 million, or one in five Americans. But that number doesn't begin to tell the whole story. The fastest growing age group is people 85 +. By 2050, people 60 and older will outnumber children for the first time in human history. Here in the U.S., 10,000 people a day are turning 65, and this trend will continue for the next 17 years.

This is a remarkable achievement. We have added more years to average life expectancy since 1900 than in all of history up to that time combined. We owe this unprecedented progress to incredible advances in acute care that reduced death rates among children and young adults and made it possible for people to live productively with conditions that would have killed them a generation earlier. Our medical and healthcare professions have brought us new procedures, new drugs, new prosthetics and new research that have improved the lives of millions. As a society, we also made a decision to create a system for providing adequate medical care to older persons through Medicare and to the poor and disadvantaged through Medicaid, and we invested in improvements in public health (e.g., sanitation, hygiene, living conditions, clean air and drinking water, smoking cessation, improvements in diet and exercise, etc.). The result of all of these advances is that a child born in 2011 could expect to live 78.7 years, more than 31 years longer than a child born in 1900, when life expectancy was 47—and many will live well into their 90s and beyond.[2]

The vast number of people with advanced illness will be in these older age groups. They will grapple with multiple conditions that interact in complex ways, including heart disease, stroke, cancer, diabetes and Alzheimer's disease. A Health and Human Services (HHS) initiative directed at the one in four Americans with two or more chronic diseases indicates that these individuals are at greater risk for unnecessary hospitalizations, adverse drug reactions and conflicting medical advice that may be overwhelming to patients and families.[3] Yet, only two percent of nurses and two percent of social workers specialize in geriatric fields. There are only about 6,750 geriatricians practicing in this country— roughly one for every 2,800 Americans over age 75.

As society ages: more older people will live alone; women will be a larger proportion of the elderly population; older people will be more dispersed geographically; and less informal support will be available in the community to care for the elderly as children and other relatives tend to live away from older family members. Two-thirds of caregivers are women, with an average age of 48. Eighty-six percent are taking care of a relative; one-third care for two or more people; over a third are taking care of a parent; and they've been in their role an average of 4.6 years. For caregivers of adults, the average age of the persons they are caring for is 69.3, and over half are 75 or older. According to a study by AARP and the National Alliance for Caregiving, more than three in ten households reported at least one person has served as an unpaid family caregiver within the last year. That means there are over 36.5 million households in the U.S. with a caregiver present. The 2012 Genworth Cost of Care Survey estimates that seven out of ten people age 65 and over will need some kind of long-term care lasting 90 days or older.

Alzheimer's disease is increasingly taking a toll. It is not caused by age alone, but it becomes more likely with age. The Alzheimer's Association reports that one out of four people age 85 and older have the disease and that one out of three people over 65 who die today have Alzheimer's or some form of dementia. As our population ages and people live longer, the sheer number of people projected to suffer from Alzheimer's could mushroom from just over five million today to more than 16 million by mid-century —unless we find ways to control the disease.

Thus, the aging of America is having a profound effect on our society— certainly not all for the bad—but when it comes to advanced illness care, the challenges are formidable.

In addition, as we brace for the coming wave of older Americans with progressive chronic illness, we must address the fragmentation in our health system: the care delivery in separate, loosely affiliated silos, which present a bewildering maze to patients, whether in hospitals (that provide high-tech, curative treatment), in physician offices and clinics (that address acute complaints) or long–term care facilities (that provide rehabilitation and/or skilled nursing) among others. All of these siloes contribute to substandard care, personal and family hardship, and inefficiencies in care delivery. While reforming advanced illness care is vitally important for patients, it is important to recognize that it affects everyone, imposing emotional and financial burdens on families, friends, co-workers and society. As such, transforming advanced illness care in America requires a comprehensive approach that includes: identifying and implementing proven clinical models of care, engaging the public, patients and families and caregivers in the discussion, expanding the role of the faith community and spiritual leaders, educating clinicians and other professionals in communication and interpersonal skills, implementing legislative and regulatory change at the federal and state levels, and helping employers learn how to best support employee caregivers as they navigate between caring for their loved ones and their workplace responsibilities. If we can do this, in a coordinated, cohesive way, we will create positive, sustainable change for American society.

In short, transforming advanced illness care in America requires nothing less than changing the culture around advanced illness and advanced illness care. That means changing attitudes, as well as practices and policies. We must build upon the progress that we have made over past decades to achieve our vision that all Americans with advanced illness, especially the sickest and most vulnerable, will receive comprehensive, high-quality, person- and family-centered care that is consistent with their goals and values and honors their dignity. To quote Allen Lichter, MD, CEO of the American Society of Clinical Oncology (ASCO), "What we're talking about here is self-determined care—every individual's inalienable right to determine, in advance, how they will be cared for near the end of their lives."[4]

As in the case of many social issues, America's view of advanced illness and the technical and medical approaches to care has evolved significantly over time. As Jay Mahoney, who for more than fourteen years led the National Hospice Organization (NHO) now called the National Hospice and Palliative Care Organization (NHPCO), has observed, progress in treating and caring for those with advanced illness is directly related to the acceptance and advancement of hospice care. Hospice was the original pioneer in creating patient and family-centered coordinated care for those with terminal illness. As a result, the hospice model provides a framework for those that are pre-terminal.

The unprecedented success of hospice care over the years can be attributed to the courage and conviction of the hospice movement's early leaders, to the executives and board members who have led the nation's individual hospices for more than 35 years and mostly to the thousands of volunteers and care givers who have stood at the bedside of the terminally ill fulfilling the promise that hospice care makes to its patient and families. However, despite the dedication and hard work of all of these individuals the fact remains that hospice care, if it existed at all, would be more of an ongoing social experiment rather than the integral part of the health care system that it is today. The difference between those two paths was the creation of the Medicare Hospice Benefit in the summer of 1982.

Jay Mahoney
Former Executive Director,
National Hospice Organization

See **Appendix A** for a brief history of advanced illness care and the hospice movement.

The Current State of Play

As discussed in Appendix A, the Institute of Medicine of the National Academy of Sciences issued a landmark report in 1997 titled, "Approaching Death: Improving Care at the End of Life." In another major contribution to the field, the Institute issued a follow-up report in 2014, "Dying in America: Improving Quality and Honoring Individual Preferences Near the End of Life,"[5] prepared by an expert committee co-chaired by Philip A. Pizzo, MD, the former Dean of the Stanford University School of Medicine, and David A. Walker, former U.S. Comptroller General of the United States. This new report calls for changes in policy, financing and clinical care and issues a call for national efforts to improve comprehensive and compassionate care, clinician-patient communication, advance care planning, revised payment systems, quality standards, professional training and enhanced public education, among other things. It will have a positive effect on the reform of advanced illness care in the U.S.

It is important to stress what reformed advanced illness care is **not.** It is not about rationing care. It is not about callously "pulling the plug on grandma," as some have charged. It is not about death panels deciding who will live and who will die. It's about changing a care system that is uncoordinated and chaotic. Research shows that when people with advanced illness get the information they want and need, they tend to choose less aggressive treatment and more comfort-focused care and professional and family support. Sometimes, more treatment is chosen and the health system should be supportive of such decisions that honor the patient's wishes. A physician told the story of his treating an elderly woman on a ventilator. Every week, he called the woman's daughter and said, "Your mother is not going to get better. Are you sure this is what you want for her?" And each week the daughter responded, "Please understand, doctor, we are a family that believes in miracles." In that case, the elderly woman's treatment continued as the family requested. Or think of a mother of young children who has breast cancer. She may want every possible form of treatment she can get – experimental drugs, surgery, radiation, chemotherapy – and to fight hard to the very end. She must and will be given every chance to do so. So this is not about denying treatment. Indeed, some individuals may choose more care or different care. Respecting individuals' values and wishes means allowing for the full spectrum of care from all to nothing and everything in between. Respecting and being responsive to people's wishes is about seeing that people with advanced illness and their families receive the information and support they need and receive comprehensive, patient and family-centered, high-quality care that is consistent with their values and wishes.

Fortunately, the number of advanced illness programs has increased dramatically and promising new efforts are underway that can significantly impact how patients and families plan for advanced illness care, the roles of the faith community and employers, public communication, clinical care models, education and public policy reforms. While each of these is discussed in more detail in subsequent chapters, we will provide a brief overview here to present the current state of advanced illness care.

Advance Care Planning

As evident throughout the history of advanced illness care, self-determination and respecting the wishes of the patient and family members are paramount to quality care. But, advance care planning and respecting patient choices should not be considered a stand-alone program. They are integral to the entire care system. Demonstrating how pervasive this philosophy can be, and building on the results of its *Respecting Choices* model, Gundersen Health System in La Crosse, Wisconsin redesigned its electronic record system to allow any provider to retrieve or add to a patient's care plan.[6] They recognize that not everyone is capable of talking about what kinds of care they would want in case of serious illness. For example, men more than women and people who are more religious tend to want to leave care decisions to their physicians. If collaborative care planning were to become the expected practice, some of this reticence might erode. In truth, neither families nor clinicians find these conversations easy, but ideally, they should begin far in advance of a medical crisis—around the kitchen table, rather than the ICU bed.

The content of patient/family/clinician conversations should not be built around the convenience of the health care system with yes/no choices typified by the early "living wills." Instead, these conversations are opportunities to explore personal values. Later decisions then can be guided by those values, even in the face of unanticipated circumstances and great uncertainty. The conversation should be repeated, updated, and revised as necessary as illness progresses, in light of new information or changed life circumstances, and in an environment of love and trust.

A significant finding in recent years is that campaigns focused on promoting advanced planning prior to the period in which a patient and family are dealing with serious illness appear to provide only limited, if any, benefits to the patient. Despite this research finding, some public engagement campaigns promote advance planning as the major intervention in advanced illness communication. This appears to be based on assumptions that people who have "planned in advance" can better deal with death and dying. On the contrary, there is evidence that generally healthy people do not want to discuss their "end of life" treatment until there is a need and benefit to doing so (i.e. at the time of a serious illness).

The Role of Faith Communities

Spirituality is a vital component of care for many people with advanced illnesses and their caregivers. Clergy can help people heal, even when cure is not possible. Through partnerships with health systems, it is clear that the faith community is a critical link to reaching those in society who often are underserved during serious illness. In many communities characterized by low socioeconomic status and associated disparities in access to care, the church and other religious institutions tie the community together and often also function as the de facto provider of services that help to maintain health, stability, and spiritual welfare. Finally, a strong presence of the faith community in national and regional partnerships can provide moral authority to improve advanced illness care for the vulnerable in society. What is becoming evident is that faith communities have the potential to expand their roles with other community resources for both patients and providers, and to become a central point for health education and informed decision-making. This is discussed further in Chapter 3, "The Role of Spirituality."

The Role of Employers

The demands of caregiving are a growing issue for employers, as more employees take on the role of caring for aging parents and other loved ones. Caregiving (and, ultimately, bereavement) frequently reduce employees' productivity, contribute to absenteeism, "presenteeism," stress-related health problems, and turnover. In the long run, caregiving issues and advance care planning should become part of the normal conversation with trained human resources and employee assistance personnel, especially among health care employers. Some companies already are responding to this challenge with employee information, flexible policies, and connections to local resources.[7] As more and more employers take an active role in supporting employee caregivers, there is a positive effect on employee well being, less absenteeism and stress and improved morale. Best practices generally go beyond typical Employee Assistance Programs (EAP) and include paid time off, flexibility in scheduling; geriatric care manager services and consultations; specific workplace programs with employee feedback; volunteer programs; and fostering a corporate culture that embraces work/life benefits. The role of employers is discussed in more detail in Chapter 4.

Public Communication

There are a number of national (e.g., *The Conversation Project*) and regional (e.g., *Honoring Choices* in Minneapolis/St. Paul) initiatives aimed at building public will for change and empowering people to make informed plans and decisions for advanced illness. These initiatives, including C-TAC's, are often focused on: encouraging families and individuals to have end-of-life care discussions and document those discussions before emergencies occur; and educating people about specific care options along the advanced illness continuum.

Patients and their families tend to have high levels of information needs at all stages of the progression of a serious illness. This involves care and treatment (the nature of the illness, likely symptoms and their management, treatment options and their pros and cons and potential outcomes). Other important information needs include care giving, spiritual support and financial/legal planning. However, regarding care and treatment, there is no common language of health and medical terms among patients, families and caregivers, nor among health professionals, who often assign different meanings and interpretations to the same concepts.

In addition, the majority of Americans do not appear to understand their care options in the event of serious illness. And family caregivers, who are critical players in times of advanced illness, are too often peripheral to the formal treatment of the ill person and are often excluded from the process of decision-making.

Patients and their families are as diverse as any other segment of American society. Asian Americans, African Americans, Hispanics and white Americans tend to have somewhat differing views of advanced illness and end of life and different cultural perspectives and resulting treatment and care giving choices. Understanding these nuances is important in effective communications.

The emphasis in public engagement initiatives should focus on individual/family empowerment, quality of life, and excellence of care. Focusing on the care improvements that patient will receive appears better received and more acceptable than emphasizing potential cost savings.

In the anxiety and stress of facing illness in our medical institutions, the fact that hospice care actually provides more care and that people receiving hospice care generally live longer than those receiving aggressive treatment is frequently lost on the public. Our current medical approach often deems "more care" to mean more aggressive care when in reality palliative and hospice care provides more contact, more frequent communication, and a more comprehensive team around them. The hospice model provides important lessons for how Americans living with advanced illness should be cared for.

In the end, experience has taught us that communication with the public requires a long-term, broad-based effort. It should involve many types of community forces working collaboratively, including the faith community and employers; and the effort should use a full array of communications vehicles—broadcast, print, the Internet, social media, and interpersonal. Specific approaches must be tailored to the unique resources and population demographics of each community.

A C-TAC paper, issued in January 2014 titled, "Consumer Perceptions and Needs Regarding Advanced Illness Care: Are we Listening?", addresses a number of the issues related to effective public engagement.

Models That Work

Acting on patient and family choices depends on having effective care systems in place that create shared and informed decision-making between patients and clinicians that allow those choices to be honored. System innovations are beginning to change the health care landscape for patients with advanced illnesses, providing alternatives to the current fragmented and often inadequate care system.[8] These models emphasize the value of care coordination and other aspects of quality and the careful alignment of services with patient values and wishes. For example:

- Aetna's Compassionate Care program includes a liberalized hospice benefit, emphasizes quality of care, and trains nurse case managers to work with patients and families. One outcome has been a dramatic increase in hospice enrollment and days in hospice care.[9]

- Allina Health System's LifeCourse program is focused on the development of an ongoing, personal relationship with a non-clinical Care Guide and utilizes an interdisciplinary team to address all domains of palliative care and to coordinate care across all settings and care partners. Allina views its model as a complement to existing services and to the existing strengths and assets of people with advanced illness and their caregivers.

- The Hospice Innovations Group, a collective of approximately 20 innovative, non-profit hospice programs across the country, has also identified best practices for leveraging the competencies of hospice care and applying them to high quality advanced illness care models. Components of these models include care coordination, consultations for palliative care and new service lines, such as PACE, transitions, house calls, complementary therapy, and social programs. In addition, The Innovations Group compiles meaningful outcome measures, with multiple providers reporting standardized real-time electronic data used to facilitate better clinician performance and to fast track program improvement.

- Kaiser Permanente has tested an advanced illness care model in three randomized controlled trials. This model increases access to specialty trained palliative support, embeds specialists in high-risk settings, systematically addresses care planning, and is developing complex medical homes for the most seriously ill enrollees.

- The Sutter Medical Network, through its nationally recognized AIM program, provides people more choice, overcoming fragmentation and using telemedicine, among other tools, to help families provide more effective home care. Participating physicians recognize that care is better and that their patients receive services that otherwise would be uneconomical for them to offer.[10]

These and other models of advanced illness care have shown that it is possible to improve care in many dimensions and to align it more closely with patient and family wishes, as indicated by high satisfaction scores. Uniquely, these advanced illness models both increase the care quality and the patient/family experience and lower costs by:

- Better care coordination, which reduces repeated and unnecessary tests;
- Effective home support, which results in better symptom control and reduces the need for physician visits, 911 calls, hospital readmissions, and ICU days;
- Improved communication and exploration of choices, which leads to greater hospice utilization; and
- Increased efficiency across providers (for example, by providing data on referral facilities' hospital readmission rates, which encourages referral to more effective providers).

Such enhanced services are ripe for greater implementation through medical homes and Accountable Care Organizations (ACOs). The testing of additional care models also is encouraged by the Affordable Care Act (ACA). Ideally, new models would incorporate robust incentives, generate data useful for program enhancement and replication, and leverage the best practices of existing clinical models to scale successful programs nationally.

These models also indicate that steps can be taken to strengthen the care continuum, providing a "hospice-like" inter-professional team that takes a holistic and comprehensive approach to care, supporting the medical, psychosocial, and other needs of persons with advanced illness and their families and creating a seamless transition into hospice at the appropriate time.

Some of these clinical models are focused broadly to impact quality of care, quality of life and cost of care. These models often include: coordinating care across settings; providing both curative and palliative care; systematic approaches to care planning; and creating a bridge to hospice. Others are more targeted, choosing to focus on a particular setting (e.g., home, hospital, skilled nursing facility) or stage of illness (e.g., chronic condition vs. terminal condition).

To build on these promising models, The Advanced Care Project (a partnership of the AHIP Foundation's Institute for Health Systems Solutions (IHSS) and C-TAC) is underway with a number of health plans, health systems and other providers to identify, analyze and compare best practice clinical care models and to promote the results of this work to health care systems and other participants across the U.S. The project will also outline key features of payment models that align financial incentives and encourage best practices. All this is discussed more fully in Chapter 5.

Professional Engagement

Physicians and nurses are trained primarily in and for acute care settings, where the intense focus is on the tests or procedures to be performed to control disease and if possible, achieving a cure. Although an increasing number of medical residents have rotations through hospice, medical training may be insufficient to fully understand the needs of an advanced illness patient.

In his book *The Best Care Possible*, palliative care physician Ira Byock says, "Even in otherwise excellent medical centers, conscientious professionals lack key skills that are essential for comprehensive caring… the unwavering treatments for sustaining life can leave someone who is living with an advanced illness physically uncomfortable, feeling lost and confused, not knowing how to get through each day or how to plan for the future…it is not easy to die well in modern times."Patients and families, too, are inculcated with the belief that there is always something more that can be done. Understanding that the patient may derive greater benefit from pulling back on tests and interventions is an educational challenge for both patient and clinician. Nor are clinicians generally taught enough about working effectively in multidisciplinary teams; yet team approaches are a hallmark of good palliative care and essential to managing transitions and avoiding re-hospitalizations.[11] In the Accountable Care Organization (ACO) environment, teamwork will be increasingly valued. Clinicians, especially physicians, need help in learning how to communicate uncertainty. In general, they greatly overestimate a patient's survival prospects. In addition, chaplains, other clergy, and other professional groups from whom patients and families seek advice may need special training to participate effectively in and to normalize "the conversation." In some locales, parish nurses, retired nurses, and teachers have been taught to lead discussions on end-of-life preferences.

There are tested, quality training resources available that improve clinician training and patient/family outcomes. One example is the work being directed by Helen McNeal at the Institute for Palliative Care at California State University San Marcos.

Yet many clinicians are not accessing these programs or tools and/or need additional training in communication and interpersonal skills to provide person-centered care for advanced illness. In addition, the culture of our health system does not always foster or promote needed competencies for appropriate patient-family/clinician decision-making. Chapter 2, "Putting Patients and Families First," addresses these issues in detail.

Policy Reforms

Progress has been made in enacting public policies to better support advanced illness care, but it is clear that further legislative and regulatory change at federal and state levels is needed to advance the key strategies for change (public engagement, best practice clinical models, professional engagement and support). At a National Summit on Advanced Illness Care in January 2013, U.S. Senators Isakson (R-GA), Warner (D-VA) and Whitehouse (D-RI) expressed interest in taking up this challenge. Congressman Blumenauer (D-OR), Engel (D-NY), Senator Wyden (D-OR), and former Senator Blanche Lincoln are also involved. Of course, there are always challenges at the Federal level, including the need for bipartisanship and the importance of solidarity among the community of advanced illness reformers in advocating for policy action.

There is a need for a clear, consensus roadmap for policy reform, which includes: identifying specific policy barriers and the needed solutions to fundamental system change; building bipartisan support at state and federal levels; and strong policy advocacy backed by public opinion, founded on a grassroots and movement for action.

Late in 2013 a policy report was issued by C-TAC, titled "Advanced Illness Policy Review: The Landscape for Improving Advanced Illness Care in America." It is a compendium of federal policy bills proposed over recent years to improve care for people with serious illness and providing support for those who care for them. The purpose of the report was to establish the current state of play with regard to policy analysis and to assess the range of options that can impact and improve advanced illness care. The next step was to create a broadly supported, comprehensive policy agenda at the national level, released in late 2014, to address ways to:

- Adopt care models that honor individual care choices, wishes, and preferences;
- Improve the alignment of payment systems;
- Improve incentives for more efficient, higher quality care across the continuum of an illness that rewards for value, rather than volume of care delivery;
- Increase provider awareness and engagement;
- Ensure that a comprehensive range of supports and services are offered to families and caregivers;
- Design flexible benefit options in order to accommodate diverse individual circumstances while requiring certain minimum standards and benefits; and
- Strengthen the current **hospice benefit** to preserve the movement's original intent and to actively participate in building a more compassionate, efficient and responsive health care system for Americans living with advanced illness by strengthening the care continuum and reinforcing the care bridge for the terminally ill into hospice.

Chapter 6, "Policy and Advocacy," contains a more detailed discussion of a policy framework.

The Challenges and Opportunities Ahead

Dr. Martin Luther King, Jr., once observed, "All progress is precarious, and the solution of one problem brings us face-to-face with another problem."[12] While considerable progress has been made in transforming advanced illness care in America, we also see that we are now face-to-face with additional problems that must be solved in order to close that gap between what people want when they are seriously ill and what they receive instead. Three stories illustrate this point.

Another trip to the emergency room in the middle of a frigid night was not what my Mom wanted, nor was it what my sister, Melinda, and I wanted for her. Our mother was a proud woman who had lived independently for years with multiple chronic conditions. However, she was 85 years old, frail and, on this night, had the symptoms of a mild stroke, so what else could we do? This was a recurring cycle over many years. Late at night, when the doctor's office closed, simple answers to simple questions did not come quickly, but were rather discovered only after putting Mom through tiresome rounds of E.R. protocol (C.T. scans, M.R.I's and countless forms to fill out). Finding answers during "business hours" wasn't much easier. Communication among the numerous specialists treating Mom was seriously lacking. Although I had worked in health care for almost all my life, we felt wholly unprepared, distressed and lost -- until Mom enrolled in hospice care. The hospice team from Capital Caring was extraordinary and gave her the quality of life, respect and dignity she deserved.

—Tom Koutsoumpas

My brother called while my wife and I were at a memorial service for my mother-in-law in Montana. Our father had suffered a stroke. He was transferred from one hospital to another, and the doctors there said that Dad should be put into an intensive care unit immediately. They might be able to stop the bleeding and stabilize him. We agreed that this isn't what he told us he wanted, but how could we pass up a chance to save his life? What should we do? We went along with the doctors' advice. After a very difficult, torturous week, it was clear that he wasn't going to get better. Two hours after we set up a hospice care arrangement (a team came in from outside the hospital) Dad died.

—Bill Novelli

"...the costs for my mother, who is 86 and who, for the past 18 months, has not been able to walk, talk, or to address her most minimal needs and who...is absent short-term memory, come in at about $ 17,000 a month. And while her long-term care insurance hardly covers all of that, I'm certainly grateful she had the foresight to carry such a policy. ...[but] long-term care insurance helps finance some of the greatest misery and suffering human beings have yet devised.

Everybody would manage his or her parent's decline differently. We all mess it up. We agreed with a cardiologist to perform surgery on my mother when she was 84. It did not once occur to us to say: "You want to do major heart surgery on an 84-year old woman showing progressive signs of dementia? Are you nuts?

The operation absolutely repaired my mother's heart. 'She can live for years,' according to the surgeon (who we were never to see again). But

> *before, where we were gently sinking, now we were in free fall. She was reduced to a terrified creature – losing language skills by the minute. "She certainly appears agitated," the psychiatrist sent to administer anti-psychotic drugs told me, "and so do you." Six weeks and something like $ 250,000 in hospital bills later (paid by Medicare – or that is, by you) she was returned, a shadow being, to…her assisted living apartment."*
>
> —Michael Wolff, writing about his family in the May 20, 2013 issue of New York Magazine.

As we see, our system fails us, despite the best efforts of all involved. There has to be, and there is, a better way. The other point that these stories illustrate is that advanced illness care is so intensely personal. Everyone has a story. And more often than not, the story is a negative one, often a nightmare. It's usually a story about the frustration people faced in dealing with a health care system that didn't meet their needs, a story about the anger they felt when they didn't get the care they thought they were going to receive for their mothers, fathers and others. It is often a story about the neglect their loved one experienced while in a health care facility, a story of bewilderment when faced with care options they could not comprehend, or a story about the emotional stress they endured while having to care for a loved one suffering from an advanced illness.

As we move forward with this reform movement, we are often asked, "Why now…why do you think this huge problem can be solved now after so many years of dysfunction and poor care and poor outcomes? There are good answers to the question. First, a real movement is underway, built on the pioneering work that went on for decades before. Health systems, consumer groups like the American Heart Association, AARP, the American Cancer Society and others, hospice and palliative care organizations, faith-based institutions, health insurance companies and many others are involved. They believe the time is right for sustainable change, and they are working to make it happen.

Second, the millions of care givers we talked about earlier are wiser for their experiences. They saw what their parents and other loved ones went through, and they don't want any part of it for themselves. And many of these caregivers are Baby Boomers—the enormous population cohort (78 million strong) born between 1946 and 1964. The oldest of the Boomers is now 68 and, because of the huge size of this group, nobody has been written about, catered to or analyzed more than the Boomers. They have deeply influenced every institution and stage of life they have encountered and they're not done yet. As they enter their older years, the Boomers are almost surely not going to accept the status quo of unnecessary and inappropriate care, the frequent trips in and out of emergency rooms and intensive care units, the pain and misery and suffering of their parents' generation. The Boomers are a force for change.

And as we said, everyone, Boomers and all the rest of us, has a story. This isn't a partisan or political football, not a red or blue issue. People of all walks of life—rich and poor, U.S. Senators, you and your family, everyone—have a story, and this binds us together and will bring us together to say, "enough is enough."

Change is already occurring. The once unmentionable issue of talking about the end of life is entering the mainstream. Sometimes that change can be pretty original, even quirky. Michael Hebb and his colleagues at The University of Washington have created a program called, "Let's Have Dinner and Talk About Death," which is designed to foster constructive conversations about end-of-life decisions. And in 2012, Lizzy Miles, a social worker in Columbus, Ohio, started what she calls the first "Death Café" in the United States; it's a space where people can come and talk about the subject in a safe, comfortable setting. The first death café was held in 2011, and now more than 300 are operating around the world.

Another good reason for change is that the current approach to advanced illness isn't just broken, it is truly unsustainable—in part, because it creates unnecessary costs. We can't afford to continue these increasing costs to taxpayers, to government, to the health system, and most importantly, to families and individuals. Providing high-quality care that is consistent with the wishes and values of individuals with advanced illness could result in cost savings for these individuals and their families and the health care system. The number one concern for people when they think about serious illness is the fear of that financial burden for themselves and their families, and medical costs are the number one cause of individual bankruptcy in the U.S.[13] And while family burdens are paramount, unnecessary, inappropriate advanced illness care is a significant part of the Medicare spend that affects all taxpayers.

So the time is right, the stars are aligned and we know what to do: ensure that the proper resources are available to help individuals make informed care decisions, create public pressure for change; provide support for health professionals to improve their practices and the health system, build on what already works – the clinical models that are already showing impressive results; and finally, change legislative and regulatory policies at the federal and state levels, including payment and reimbursement reform, research, standards of care and other important areas.

This is the way social change happens—bottom up and top down, with a powerful set of needs and a movement, built on a public attitude that enough is enough. The following chapters set out the details for this critically important national priority.

SECTION II

THE KEY ELEMENTS OF REFORM

CHAPTER 2

Putting Patients and Families First
Nancy Taylor
Vice President, Public Policy, External Relations,
Communications at Kaiser Permanente

"Every story tells a story that has already been told."
— Umberto Eco, Postscript to the Name of the Rose

"I will tell you something about stories . . . They aren't just
entertainment. Don't be fooled. They are all we have, you
see, all we have to fight off illness and death."
— Leslie Marmon Silko, Ceremony

At this point in my career, I have become somewhat of an expert in the issues of public policy and communications related to advanced illness and end-of-life care. And, I have always thought of myself as being well-equipped to navigate this terrain in my own life. But nothing prepares you for dealing with these issues with your own parents.

My mom died from cancer in 2011 and my father has been in and out of the hospital more times than I can count in the last five years. There are moments etched in my memory—in waiting rooms and exam rooms with doctors, sitting next to a parent on a gurney in the emergency room, late nights in surgery waiting rooms and recovery rooms, tense days in ICUs—where topics were avoided or not considered, where euphemisms were favored over directness, and where anxiety, fear and confusion prevailed. I found myself compartmentalizing. There was the daughter Nancy and the sister Nancy and these Nancys were quite distinct from the policy and communications professional Nancy.

Navigating serious illness and preparing for death is messy and complex. I have wished for "right" answers where none were available and clarity when it was not to be found. I have wanted to know what the future would hold and to have a thorough understanding of how a disease would progress. Five weeks before my mom died, she had cataract surgery. Two weeks before she died, she had a chemotherapy treatment. Were these the right decisions given the progression of her illness? Maybe, maybe not. Did we have those tough conversations as a family? Or with physicians? No. Policy Nancy would have encouraged it, but daughter Nancy didn't touch it.

My mom had read Atul Gawande's article "Letting Go," and she understood palliative care and hospice care. She knew what she wanted. She was most afraid of being in pain, and she was particularly concerned about specific kinds of pain given her unique cancer. Her care team helped us through it all. She died a peaceful, pain-free death at home with a view of her beloved garden.

My father is also aware of the choices he faces and their implications. He talks often of quality of life in making those choices. He and I have openly discussed different scenarios for his future health, and he has expressed his wishes for those circumstances. These conversations have included some of the most meaningful and fulfilling moments out of a lifetime with my father. It took some courage to broach the subject, but after we got going—and with a martini to loosen things up—the exchange was easy.

I believe the landscape is changing, and stories like mine are being shared more often and more openly. The media covers end-of-life choices, over-treatment, coordination of care, and patient-centered care in a very different light from even ten years ago. My friends speak of their own parents. Politicians debate the issues with a greater degree of civility and respect. Communities launch campaigns. Organizations like C-TAC are created, with new members joining every month. People are realizing that this is an issue that transcends politics and ideology. We are, I hope, experiencing a culture shift. A culture shift that I hope will bring policy Nancy and daughter Nancy into a more comfortable co-existence.

One development that has helped change the landscape dramatically is the widespread availability of hospice care. While hospice care is often thought to be centuries old, modern hospice care actually began in 1967, with the first American hospice established in Connecticut in 1971 (see Appendix A for a brief history of hospice). Even though some hospices have their own inpatient facilities, hospice is a philosophy of care rather than a physical place of care. The hospice philosophy of care is based on an interdisciplinary approach to care that includes physician and nursing services as well as social work; spiritual care; and occupational, physical and speech therapies. It emphasizes palliation of the pain and symptoms that result from a terminal disease, regardless of whether those symptoms are the result of physical, emotional or spiritual concerns.

Since that first hospice outside of New Haven, Connecticut, more than 5,000 hospice organizations have appeared and today serve more than 1.65 million people.[14] The success and growth of hospice care can be attributed in large part to its dynamic pioneers, the availability of the Medicare Hospice Benefit (enacted as part of the Tax Equity and Fiscal Responsibility Act of 1982) and the aging of the population. But the real catalyst for the growth and acceptance of hospice is that its philosophy and overarching principles are in tune with what patients and their families want and need. In short, they put the patient and family first by:

- Emphasizing patient self-determination and a desire to direct one's own decisions about his or her care at the end of life, focusing on the quality of that life versus simply its longevity;
- Focusing hospice care on the patient and his/her family regardless of how that family is defined or identified. From their modern day beginnings, hospice caregivers knew and appreciated that the suffering of the patient is only compounded by isolating the

patient from the family, and that the suffering of the family—for too long simply ignored by traditional medicine—only results in increased morbidity for those family members;

- Delivering on the promise of hospice care: assuring patients that they will not die alone, that they will not die in pain, and that their care will not become an unbearable burden on their loved ones.

Another part of this landscape change is driven by storytelling. Storytelling is an age-old tradition and one of the most effective ways human beings have to communicate. Stories create a shared experience. They connect us. Stories convey information in vivid and accessible ways, and stories can spark a deeper understanding of ideas and events.

Stories on the topic of illness and death are no exception. They are mixed in tone, sometimes triumphant and sometimes devastating. And, they are emerging from a dark corner in our public discourse. They less often seem a topic or a place to avoid. Stories about personal experiences with illness and the process of dying are now being shared more publicly, more often, more easily and in ever more varied settings, from the kitchen table in a farm house in Iowa, to the patient room in a hospital in Seattle, and to the halls of Congress.

Why do these stories about dying and illness matter? They matter because we, as a society and as individuals, are reflected in the stories we tell. Stories test boundaries, explore norms and beliefs, shift perspectives, provide opportunities to learn, and ultimately create a national dialogue about an issue. In this case, the issue is a delicate one that includes declining health and well-being, pain and suffering, the last years of life, and death. Some of the stories also touch on the joy, humanity and connection that can reveal itself along that same path. And that is what we strive for—hoping that those stories of grace and dignity in the face of advanced illness and death will outnumber the stories of confusion, pain and suffering. In highlighting the intensely personal experience in the face of illness, we can identify the opportunities to improve that experience. We can create change.

At the heart of each story is the question of choices and how to ensure that one's personal values are reflected in the management of illness, and in some cases, in decisions about how to approach death. These stories often include themes of confusion in navigating an illness and in trying to coordinate between physicians and hospitals and insurance companies. Getting a diagnosis is often a time-consuming process filled with misunderstandings and gaps in communications that contribute to an already stressful situation for the patients and families making their way through the process.

Different individuals will have different beliefs and preferences regarding advanced illness and what maximizes the quality of life in the final months or years. Each person's preferences are unique. Therefore, an individual's personal preferences, values, beliefs and cultural norms must be considered as part of any treatment plan. For that reason, it is critical that the patient and family are put first and that their values are taken into account at every step along the way. Excellent care must be patient-centered care. Anything less than patient-centered care is less than excellent care. Dr. Don Berwick puts it elegantly in his 2009 article in *Health Affairs* titled, "What Patient-Centered Should Mean: Confessions of an Extremist."

> What chills my bones is indignity. It is the loss of influence on what happens to me. It is the image of myself in a hospital gown, homogenized, anonymous, powerless, no longer myself. It is the sound of a young nurse calling me, "Donald," which is a name I never use—its "Don," or, for him or her, "Dr. Berwick." It is the voice of the doctor saying, "We think...," instead of, "I think...," and thereby placing that small verbal wedge between himself as a person and myself as a person. It is the clerk who tells my wife to leave my room, or me to leave hers, without asking if we want to be apart. Last month, a close friend called a clinic for her mammogram report and was told, "You have to come here; we don't give that information out on the telephone."

She said, "It's OK, you can tell me." They said, "No, we can't do that." Of course, they "can" do that. They choose not to, and their choice trumps hers: period. That's what scares me: to be made helpless before my time, to be made ignorant when I want to know, to be made to sit when I wish to stand, to be alone when I need to hold my wife's hand, to eat what I do not wish to eat, to be named what I do not wish to be named, to be told when I wish to be asked, to be awoken when I wish to sleep. Call it patient-centeredness, but, I suggest, this is the core: it is that property of care that welcomes me to assert my humanity and my individuality.[15]

Americans have generally shied away from conversations about advanced illness and the process of dying, but a shift seems to be underway. Over the past few years, journalists and others have published their own stories and thoughts on the challenges in advance care planning, often in beautifully written and heartfelt pieces. In addition to Dr. Berwick's article cited above, notable articles include: Atul Gawande's "Letting Go: What Should Medicine Do When It Can't Save Your Life?"[16] from *The New Yorker*; Michael Wolf's piece "A Life Worth Ending"[17] from *New York Magazine*; and Charles Ornstein's reflections captured in *The Washington Post* article "How Mom's Death Changed my Views on End of Life Care,"[18] to name just a few. These types of articles are shifting the public discourse. Along with organized initiatives like The Conversation Project (http://theconversationproject.org/)[19], Honoring Choices (http://www.honoringchoices.org/)[20], and television programs like the Frontline Series on "Facing Death," (http://www.pbs.org/wgbh/pages/frontline/facing-death/)[21] they help move the conversation into living rooms and kitchens across the country. These initiatives are dedicated to encouraging individuals, families and communities to have discussions about their wishes and choices for end-of-life care. Because of these initiatives (and others like them that are emerging throughout the country), it is becoming more routine and more acceptable to speak of the difficult choices that we face. Under what circumstances should a feeding tube be inserted? How does one decide when to remove life support? What factors contribute to a decision to perform heart surgery on an 85-year-old with dementia? How does a family begin to make that type of choice?

At the heart of all of these stories are the patients and their families. There is the periodic story of the doctor as a hero, or medical technology as the hero. But more often, the physician is portrayed as a guide or partner, sometimes effective and sometimes not. Many people are realizing that they need and want to be more involved in the management of their care. They want to decide what works for them and what doesn't. But not everyone desires that level of engagement—some like the idea that their physician or nurse will take the lead on important decisions. Either way, that choice is a preference that should be honored. For providers, figuring out those preferences and guiding a patient through difficult illness or end of life is a challenge, but it can also provide some of the most meaningful and fulfilling aspects of the profession. For the patient, articulating those preferences in concert with loved ones can be difficult, and making difficult choices in the heat of the moment is even more harrowing. But this is an endeavor that can make all the difference in providing meaning and comfort to patients in a way that is also effective and trusted.

There is a small but growing body of research on the public attitudes about advanced illness and the patient and provider experience in caring for the elderly, or anyone with a serious illness. A thorough understanding of that research is important to designing care systems that can reflect those attitudes and to forming public policy that best supports the individuals in need as they move through this phase of life.[22] That research tells us that a particularly difficult issue is confusion about the terminology related to advanced illness, primarily among patients but even among medical professionals.[23] We don't have a common understanding of some of the most basic terms. For example, many people—physicians and the general public alike—are under the impression that palliative care is, quite simply, end-of-life care. In actuality, palliative care is care that is designed to reduce suffering and enhance quality of life, regardless of whether a patient is undergoing curative treatments or is close to end of his or her life. In addition, there is a gap between the language that health care professionals use and that which patients are able to understand (or that matters most them). For example, it is easy to find lists of the services that Medicare covers, but less easy to find a list of items that are not covered, which may come as a surprise to patients and their families.

Recent research shows that many people would choose a shorter, higher-quality life over a longer, lower-quality life.[24] In addition, surveys indicate that the majority of people would prefer to stay in their homes with their families to support them and provide them with the care they need rather than to be in hospitals, nursing homes or other settings. Most patients indicate that their highest preferences are the desire to spend quality time with family and friends, to have their pain managed, to have their spiritual wishes and needs respected, and to be assured that loved ones are not emotionally and financially devastated by their illness or death. But even with these preferences—and knowing that they could be at risk—few people actually have the conversations or do the planning required to make certain that these preferences are understood by their families or health care providers. It is a conversation that brings up uncertainty and difficult topics, and so more often than not, it becomes a conversation that is avoided. As a country, we need to put in place systems and controls that enable and facilitate these conversations early so that every individual can have those preferences honored and respected.

The research also shows that many elderly Americans articulate fears of being a burden on their families.[25] The cost of treatment is a key concern, ranking higher even than being unprepared for dying spiritually, according to a study reported in JAMA.[26] There is a common theme of fear around creating huge financial hardship due to a serious illness— wiping out their own life savings and leaving large bills to be paid by their families.

Adding to the predicament, families often overestimate the coverage and support that will be provided by Medicare and private insurance.

For example, many families are surprised to discover that help for bedridden patients is not considered a medical need and will not be covered by Medicare. Discovering these issues in the midst of advanced illness towards the end of one's life creates additional stresses on an already difficult situation.

As an illness progresses, the communication between patients, families (who are often also caregivers), and providers becomes even more critical. The lack of a shared language combined with emotionally trying times make these communications progressively more difficult. Patients are looking for guidance in making decisions, and they increasingly count on their providers and caregivers as the disease progresses. Likewise, as family members provide more and more of the care for patients as illnesses progress, their information requirements change—they need more information and on different subjects. When their loved ones are in the early stages of needing care, family caregivers provide mostly personal care and do household chores. But as the illness progresses, family caregivers are called upon to provide more medical care more frequently. This is a much more complicated role. They are often coordinating the medical care among providers and communicating directly with physicians. They are also likely to be managing medications, IVs and injections, and wound care. They are managing equipment use and ensuring availability of supplies. So not only do they need information to help them care for patients, they also need support for the many additional emotional and social burdens they now face.

Providers have equally challenging circumstances. They must gauge the preferences of each individual patient, understand the role the patient wishes their physician or nurse to play (and there is most assuredly variation in this regard), and they must assess the amount and timing of information to provide to patients. There is often a large gap between how much a physician may know about an illness and what a patient may know, but the most effective decision making in these instances is when that gap is effectively bridged and decisions are made jointly between all of the parties involved.

The challenges we face in addressing these communication gaps and honoring the preferences of patients are enormous. While we must continue to learn about these preferences and challenges through studies and surveys, we already know some things about what works and what doesn't. Research shows that younger and healthier people resist discussing "end-of-life" treatments or completing advance directives, preferring to wait until such a discussion is "truly" needed, such as after an illness has been diagnosed.[27] Even when advance directives have been completed, they often have little effect on treatment decisions that occur once patients have lost the ability to make their own decisions. For this reason, the recent focus of many health care systems on increasing completion rates of advance directives may be misguided or insufficient.

The POLST (Physician Orders for Life-Sustaining Treatment) paradigm appears to be a promising remedy to this situation. The National POLST Paradigm is an approach to end-of-life planning based on conversations between patients, loved ones, and health care professionals designed to ensure that seriously ill or frail patients can choose the treatments they want or do not want and that their wishes are documented and honored. A recent study published in the Journal of the American Geriatrics Society (JAGS) found that end-of-life preferences of people who do not want to be hospitalized as documented in POLST orders were honored.[28]

We do know that once a patient and his/her family are in the midst of dealing with advanced illness, their information needs are significant, and those needs are not being well met. Patients and families want information about how an illness will progress and what types of symptoms to expect, how to best manage those symptoms and what the possible treatment options will be. And they want to know how to best prepare for and manage someone's final days.

Given what we know about the challenges and the gap that we face, how do we build on the existing pockets of excellent work and the growing number of successful initiatives (see Chapter 5) to accelerate the pace of change and improve the nation's efforts in addressing the problem? A critical next step is to create a common language and understanding that will work for all of the major stakeholders involved: patients, families, caregivers, and providers.

Another important approach is to provide the various stakeholders with the information they need in ways that reflect different stages along the way. Behaviors and needs change during the course of advanced illness, but some of the information to support end-of-life decisions does not keep pace with these changes. Several efforts are underway nationally and in local communities to address this need. In addition to the *Conversation Project* and *Honoring Choices* initiatives and the POLST Paradigm mentioned previously, C-TAC has developed CareJourney.org —a consumer based website aimed at helping patients and their caregivers understand their diagnoses, what those diagnoses mean for the future, and how to plan for their care and caregiving—medically, financially and spiritually. The information on CareJourney.org comes from C-TAC member organizations and is well documented and carefully crafted. The site provides information relevant to every stage along this journey and provides a comprehensive set of links to resources that will aid consumers in making important choices. C-TAC's goal in this endeavor is to ensure that patient choice and shared decision-making are foundational in care.

That means serving "people" before "patients." Many people with advanced illness want to avoid being patients, so it's important to understand what they value and create a business model and metrics to ensure that personal goals drive clinical goals, as well as to focus on personal preferences when considering all available options for care. This requires a shift in how we think about and approach care management, advance care planning and treatment and palliation.

As a first step, we need to provide care management through interdisciplinary teams supervised by an engaged leading physician and move the focus of care from the hospital to the home and community. These interdisciplinary teams should include the individual, the family, caregivers, physicians and other clinicians, other care managers and community partners (e.g., public agencies, churches and community navigators). And the structure of these teams should encourage coordinated care across all settings as the individual's condition progresses.

At the same time, we need to promote advance care planning through continuing conversations over time at the ill-person's pace in the comfort and safety of his or her home, as well as by documenting the stated preferences for care. Then, we need to ensure that those preferences are communicated to and implemented by clinicians at all points of care.

Once an individualized care plan is developed (driven by personal preference and clinical, psychological and spiritual needs), the clinical team can provide a customized blend of disease-modifying treatment plus palliative care and can fine tune the treatment to the preferred level of symptom control, managing the tradeoffs between analgesia and sedation. The team can then also alter the care plan as preferences evolve through the progression of the illness.

While this provides a broad process for putting patients and families first, much more can and should be done. We also need to enhance research efforts to collect the most recent information regarding public perceptions about advanced illness and end-of-life care. Additional resources and efforts are necessary to support improved communications. Improvements in advanced illness communications need to focus on in-the-moment decisions and support shared decision-making. Americans are calling for it. C-TAC has conducted an assessment of current practices in informed and shared decision making to identify best practices and develop tools that can be disseminated to both clinicians and consumers (see Chapter 5).

Additionally, all health professionals, policy leaders and consumer groups must be committed to developing and taking to scale research-based training programs for health professionals on effective communications. Combined with a system to continuously update care treatment plans and integrate the ongoing conversation between patients, family members and physicians, we will most surely make progress in improving care and reducing the burden on the growing number of Americans struggling with these issues. Now is the time to find a common language that will close the communications gap among consumers, health professionals, the media and policymakers.

It is absolutely critical that we get this right. If we don't, our chances of successfully transforming advanced illness care in America are greatly diminished. The increased involvement of patients and their families, hand-in hand with providers, will help lead the way. If we do get it right, perhaps we will reach a place where Don Berwick's fears of indignity, disrespect and humiliation will be a thing of the past; perhaps we will reach a place where *daughter Nancy* and *policy Nancy* will become one. That's how I will know that we have finally succeeded.

The goal is daunting: to create an environment and a culture that encourages patients and their families to make their wishes known, to speak up when they don't understand something, to voice their frustrations, to provide a personalized experience that includes an understanding of each person's unique preferences and that treats everyone with compassion and respect, to honor their cultural needs, to provide them with the information they need when they need it and how they need it, and to ensure that care is coordinated across all of the different settings where it is provided and between the numerous physicians, nurses, caregivers and other health professionals involved. It is no small ask, but aren't we each worth it?

CHAPTER 3

The Role of Spirituality in Advanced Care
Rabbi Richard Adress and Rev. Tyrone Pitts

"We take our bodies to the hospitals and our souls to churches. The two need to meet."
—Brad Stuart, MD.

We know that the goals, values and preferences of patients and families are significantly informed by their cultural and religious traditions.[29] And many who do not formally embrace a religion or faith, still have spiritual needs when facing advanced illness.

As faith communities, we need to respond with compassion, love and support to those with advanced illnesses. We must minister to the families and loved ones of those who are in the process of transitioning from this life to the next. We must also develop moral and spiritual support systems for clinicians, physicians and caregivers who neither claim spirituality nor a faith experience, but sacrifice their lives daily to provide supportive services so that those who are transitioning from this life to the next, do so with dignity and respect.

But we cannot do this on our own. We need to broaden the table, around which partnerships extend from the community to the health system and from the health system to the community.

In order to be full partners in the process with health care systems and others, we need to explore the roles, needs, resources of places of worship, and the language that we use—especially around spirituality and the nexus with medicine. Toward this end, we will explore three questions in this chapter:

- In an increasingly secular society, what role can places of worship play in transforming advanced care?
- What is the significance of "healing" and "curing" among medical professionals and clergy and chaplains, and where does the common ground lie?
- What are the lessons learned on health systems-community partnerships from the Alameda County Care Alliance, a community-led model developed in Oakland, California?

Roles and Resources

What we as the "baby boomer" generation are experiencing more and more is the tremendous impact and contribution that the faith community plays and its vital role in the quality and dignity of life of persons that need advanced care. The following story illustrates this point.

"Watching my mother—a woman of extreme faith—transition from this life to the next was a defining moment for me in 2004. As a minister of the Gospel and a person of faith, I had witnessed many transitions over the years, but this time it was different. After being diagnosed with cancer of the liver in early November and having a stroke during an MRI procedure in early December, I saw my lively, God-fearing Christian exurban mother, who prayed daily and was always the life of the party, the greatest cook on this planet, full of laughter, excitement and wisdom, live for over a month in an almost vegetable state, only able to say a few words and occasionally squeeze my hand.

This was a painful process to watch—seeing such an exciting life smile with her eyes and give gestures of approval with only one or two words in her voice.

After spending over two hours reading the Book of Psalms to her during her transition, and seeing her comfort and subtle smile with her eyes, she peacefully closed her eyes and breathed her last breath. This was a spiritual moment that I will never forget.

As I watched her transition with peace and dignity, remaining true to her faith tradition and listening to her favorite passages of Scripture, I experience a closeness with her and the Creator, that has impacted my life ever since. These few hours experiencing the end of life with my mother remain an indelible part of my memory and my being.

From this experience, I witnessed the disconnections in relationships between the family caregiver, the service provider, the physician, the faith leaders and the community. I also witnessed the tremendous support systems that are available to persons suffering with advanced illness in houses of worship and the community."

—Tyrone Pitts

While many Americans are moving away from association with formal religion, places of worship still have important roles to play. As one pastor said in a recent meeting in San Diego, "Fewer African Americans are going to church, but whenever they have a problem or a crisis, like [when] someone's sick, they call us."

When people in crisis call, what can we provide? First and foremost, we can help provide spiritual support for the needs of patients and family caregivers, including: anxiety about an illness, tension in relationships among loved ones about care decisions, and stress and burnout. But we also need to acknowledge that we as clergy need to work collaboratively with the health care delivery team, including chaplains, in providing this spiritual support. And, as we have shown on other societal issues, we can serve as advocates for the rights and needs of the sickest and most vulnerable in society. Within this capacity, many places of worship provide an engaged, on-the-ground, organized advocacy base of health ministry workers and congregational volunteers.

As a trusted resource in the community for health and social services (such as food pantries) among vulnerable populations, places of worship can serve as hubs to add focused supportive interventions (e.g., respite care, public education, information resources, etc.) for the ill and their caregivers. In this capacity, these community hubs and the trained professionals who work in health ministries serve as extensions of the clinical care delivery team into the community. And spiritual leaders can help educate the clinical team, as well. With clinicians' increasing awareness of the cultural determinants in medical decision-making,[30] great potential exists for faith communities to help clinicians to better understand our goals, values and preferences and to provide, in turn, the community with culturally appropriate care.

As co-chairs of the C-TAC Interfaith and Diversity Workgroup, we've spoken with hundreds of clergy across the country who are ready to act and empower their community resources in partnership with health care providers, health plans and others. The time is now. We, as a body of national and regional people of faith, have come together around a common vision that states: *Ill people and their families, especially the sickest and most vulnerable living with serious illness, will receive the medical and spiritual care that matches their needs, values and goals and honors their dignity.*

Our mission in C-TAC is to develop replicable, sustainable community models to partner with health care stakeholders in improving shared and informed decision-making; providing person- and family- centered care; and improving public policy to transform the care for persons and their families living with serious illness.

Healing vs. Curing and the Importance of Spirituality

In order to achieve the Interfaith and Diversity Workgroup's grand mission, we must address the divide we in this country have unwittingly created between the care for the body and the care for the soul or the spiritual needs of the individual. Rev. J. Alfred Smith, Jr., Senior Pastor at Allen Temple Baptist Church, reminds us that, "As clergy we're always praying for healing, but healing doesn't always mean curing."

The concept of healing has theological grounding in almost all religious traditions. Clinicians and physicians are becoming more and more convinced of the fact that clergy and faith leaders play a pivotal role in helping families embrace the healing that can come through restored relationships, peace and other spiritual gifts that can be gained at the end of life. They recognize now more than ever the value of healing and the limitations of curing. For clinicians there is a reluctance to acknowledge the spiritual needs of patient and family caregivers and instead to focus on what can be done through medical science to "cure" the body of illness at all cost.

The challenge for clergy, families and clinicians is to transform the language we use to communicate and dialogue about advanced care between individuals and caregivers. We need to develop a new spiritual vocabulary that embraces a holistic understanding of personhood, incorporating diverse faith traditions, cultures and beliefs.

> *Heal us God and let us be healed, save us and let us be saved.*
> *Grant full healing to every illness, wound and pain*
> *Blessed is the Eternal who heals the sick*
>
> (Prayer for healing in the daily morning Jewish service)

Families and individuals who face the challenges associated with advanced illness often come to reality that, while no "cure" may be found, it is possible to be "healed."

That healing comes about from a spiritual growth that, even in the face of terminal illness, can provide a person and a family with a sense of acceptance and peace. They may be spiritually healed despite the truth of their physical condition. The following story illustrates this point.

> *In 2009, my father transitioned after 30 years of suffering with multiple chronic conditions. At the age of 58, he was diagnosed with COPD. After spending over 20 years in the Armed Services, he was a chain smoker and suffered from several aspects of advanced illness. In addition to having high blood pressure, he was diagnosed with bladder cancer and prostate cancer and had surgery for both.*
>
> *At the age of 79, he began using an oxygen tank on a regular basis and at age 87, he was on oxygen 24 hours a day. He often went to the emergency room on a bi-monthly basis for emergency care, and sometimes ended up in the hospital for several days. This pattern got progressively worse during the last two years of his life. Fortunately, he was a veteran and much of the cost of his hospitalization was paid for by the military.*

As his primary caregiver I recognized a chronic pattern develop during the period from 2007-2009. During this time, he was in and out of the hospital, suffered a heart attack and was put on life support and not expected to live. Unfortunately, he did not have a living will and a family dispute arose on whether or not to keep him on life support and how much time he should remain on life support. His doctor and one of the siblings recommended that he be taken off of life support because his recovery seemed unlikely.

However, the rest of the family refused to take him off of life support and after three days he fully recovered. Fortunately, he recovered and was able to live two more years of a quality of life creating excitement and joy wherever he went. I am convinced that his remarkable recovery was due to the grace of God who intervened in a healing process that resulted from much prayer, love and support from family, clergy and friends in the community. When he transitioned, he was full of life.

He decided that he wanted to leave the rehabilitation center where he was staying and have hospice at home. He refused the traditional hospital bed and decided that he wanted to stay in his own bed. He demanded that he live the remainder of his life with dignity surrounded by family and friends. We granted him his wish.

Five days after being home, while he was up walking and laughing with a friend, he had a heart attack and transitioned. He lived a quality and faithful life, full of joy and meaning.

—Tyrone Pitts

The role of spirituality in the relationship of the person and family to health care and advanced care is now returning to a more prominent position. Slowly, discussions and classes are becoming part of medical training in which medical students are being asked to confront their own spirituality and belief systems so as to make them more aware of and sensitive to the varieties of spiritual expressions that they may encounter in their practice. Dr. Don Friedman, who teaches medical students at Jefferson Medical College in Philadelphia, Pennsylvania, noted this in his essay, "Hope In The Midst of Illness:" "There is a tendency in medicine to focus on the medications and procedures to help the patient improve, a disease focus, without recognizing that patient's own capacity for hope, resilience, and healing and without awareness how the patient's belief system can help recover from a disease."[31]

The inclusion of spirituality and a person's belief system into the medical delivery model can help transform health care from a disease-oriented system into a human-relational system. Part of C-TAC's mission is to insure the sensitivity to and the inclusion of the role of spirituality in the development of health care in advanced illness situations.

If religion is an organized system of beliefs and practices, then spirituality can be seen as the way one lives out those systems of beliefs and practices on a personal level. Spirituality is personal and not institutional. It is the filter through which a person can come to a sense of personal meaning and purpose; the means a person develops to navigate the challenges of living. Because it is so personal, a health care provider needs to be sensitive to the fact that the person in front of him/her may carry a wide variety of feelings, many based on family issues, that speak to how this person in need defines his or her relationship to a "higher power."

These feelings may be based on a strong belief in a Supreme Being. They may be based on a belief in a "life force" that operates in nature. One's spirituality may be based totally on a relationship with nature or the arts; or a person's spirituality may be based on any combination of these and more. They may include a strong belief in an after-life or not. We live in an age of increasing spiritual diversity and the need to be sensitive to that diversity is growing. The growth in diverse culture within the United States will continue to create the need for health care providers to be aware of and sensitive to the diverse ways cultures may approach advanced illness and even death.

To assist health care workers, hospitals and other health delivery institutions in their awareness of a person's spiritual needs, we are seeing a gradually growing interest in developing what can be called a spiritual history. A linking of a person's medical history to a person's spiritual history and beliefs may well enhance the way medicine can better treat the whole person. If we choose to approach the patient as a whole person, then gaining an understanding of his or her belief system, or lack thereof, may be helpful in developing a relational approach to the patient that embraces the values of the dignity and sanctity of human life and the preservation of human life in dignity and sanctity. [32]

The importance of including a discussion about one's spiritual beliefs as part of a general approach to advanced illness care is borne out by the recent Pew Research Center's report on Americans' attitudes toward end-of-life care.[33] The report reinforces the statistics that we are living in an age of longevity with the life span of Americans doubling in the last century. The report cites the fact that the percentage of people over 65 has tripled in the last century to about 14 percent of our population in 2012 and is expected to reach about 20 percent by 2060. "However, roughly a quarter of the U. S. adults (27%) say they have given either no thought or not very much thought to their own wishes when it comes to end-of-life medical treatment."[34] The opportunity for houses of worship and religious institutions to be a safe place to have these conversations, based on the denominational traditions, is more and more apparent. The Pew report outlines the diversity among various groups within the country and, by implication, underscores the need for these conversations and professional trainings to take into account the diverse and pluralistic fabric of American culture.

The role of spirituality in helping people to cope with the challenges of life is continuing to find new champions. Recently, the American Psychological Association published a two-volume handbook on how best to incorporate spirituality within a therapeutic setting. The handbook's editor, Dr. Kenneth Pargament, noted that increasingly "psychologists recognize the power of religion and spirituality to help patients cope with life's challenges without becoming hopeless and depressed."[35]

The trend for mental health and physical health professionals to take into consideration their patient's spiritual beliefs and practices can only lead to a more holistic and person-centered approach to care. The late Rabbi Abraham Joshua Heschel discussed the joining of the medical and religious worlds for the benefit of the patient. In a speech titled, "The Patient as a Person," delivered to the convention of the American Medical Association in June 1964, Heschel spoke of the linkages between the physician and the clergy in a sacred context.

> *"The doctor is God's partner in the struggle between life and death. Religion is medicine in the form of prayer, medicine is prayer in the form of deed. From the perspective of the love of God, the work of healing and the work of religion are one. The body is a sanctuary, the doctor is a priest. Medicine is a sacred art. Its work is holy…It is a grievous mistake to keep a wall of separation between medicine and religion. There is a division of labor but a unity of spirit. The act of healing is the highest form of Imitatio Dei. To minister to the sick is to minister to God. Religion is not the assistant to medicine, but the secret of one's passion for medicine."[36]*

What are some of the aspects that impact someone's spirituality? One's sense of spirituality is born out of the awareness of one's own mortality. This reality of one's own mortality becomes more evident as we age. It is tied to a sense of the fragility of time and our place in it and thus allows us, if we so choose, to begin to examine the fundamental questions of life that revolve around finding our own sense of meaning and purpose. A key component of this is the fear of being alone. In Genesis 2:18, we read that it is not good for a person to be "alone." This alone-ness is the existential alone-ness that propels us to seek out relationships, create societies and families. How we choose to find our way in this becomes our spiritual pattern. It helps define who we are as human beings. Our genetic code and our family of origin also contribute to how we adapt to the challenges and varieties of life. The choices we make and how we choose all need to be factored in to how we approach advanced care and illness in order for true "healing" to take place.

This personal approach underscores the truth of our own uniqueness. No two persons are the same; no two patients are the same. This uniqueness is part of the religious approach to human life and reinforces the fact that each of us is our own world, unique unto us individually. We each carry with us our own sense of self, history, dreams, fears and beliefs. A challenge of person-centered care is to be able to be sensitive to these issues. This is not easy, especially in our current system of health care. However, this relation-centered approach can and should be a vital part of the health care-patient continuum.

This more "holistic" approach is one of the reasons that religious institutions can be valuable partners for patient care and education. These institutions recognize each person's autonomy and validate his or her own personal story. Here, individuals are part of a larger society or family of faith where relationships, from direct service to prayer, are considered part of normal practice. The role of the religious institution also helps insure the reality of diversity. With the growth of diverse cultures in our society, it is often the religious community that "speaks the language" of a person in ways a medical facility cannot. The need for this awareness of diverse cultures, practices and approaches to medical care will become even more important as the demographics of our country continue to change.

A key variable in virtually all advanced illness scenarios is hope, whether it be hope for a cure, hope for healing, hope for peace, or hope for a miracle. This is where the role of spirituality and the spiritual leader can be of even greater value. Spirituality's partner is often hope. Even in the face of a terminal illness, there is the reality we can hope for a healing of the soul. Every clergy person has seen this. Reconciliation takes place within a family. An individual finds a way to conclude his or her relationships with children or spouse. There is a "good-bye" that brings a sense of healing and release to people involved. These moments can provide a hope that one's final years or days are filled with meaning and love and not isolation and exile. Religious institutions offer pathways to hope, and how one chooses to walk those paths defines one's spirituality. Not to be aware of these paths and how people walk them misses a valuable aspect of the healing process for both patients and their loved ones.

Spiritual care for everyone is healthy and necessary to our society. Thus, it is critical to this dialogue that we advocate, affirm and encourage honest conversation, to ensure that competent, coordinated, culturally sensitive spiritual care is integrated into the health care provided across all settings for persons, their family members and their caregivers. This becomes increasingly vital as we address the needs of underserved and poor communities that have historically been excluded from health care due to institutional racism, class and gender.

Community Action Model

The Community Action model is designed to be community-based and community-led, replicable and sustainable across sites and populations around the country. Its purpose is to address the needs and challenges of persons dealing with advance illness, their families and caregivers.

Specific areas of focus for starting the advanced care program include:

- Identifying and building upon established working relationships among the faith community and health systems;
- Knowledgeable community-based advocates who will organize, support and guide the community; and supported by;
- Technical assistance to develop a strategic plan and fundraise to operationalize the plan.

The model is built on a three part foundation:

1. Evidence-based practices in advanced illness management such as: nursing/social work interventions together with synthesized proven approaches to transitional care, self-management, care coordination and palliative care. The core driver of advanced illness clinical models is a trusting relationship between the ill person, clinicians and a health care liaison. Since faith-based organizations can serve as a trusted community convener, they could naturally serve as a bridge to community resources (e.g., spiritual support, meals, etc.) with a health system's advanced illness management program and other clinical programs (see "Memphis model" below).

2. Effective models of regional community - health system partnerships such as the Congregational Health Network, in Memphis, Tennessee. Founded in 2006, the Congregational Health Network or "Memphis model" is a partnership between Methodist Le Bonheur HealthCare and 500+ places of worship designed to support transition from hospital to home for vulnerable populations in the Memphis community. As a result of the model, enrollees showed lower mortality, utilization, costs, and charges including reduction in readmissions rates and time, increased referrals to hospice and home health, and higher patient satisfaction.

The model consists of 11 paid staff (1 Director and 10 health navigators), 599 congregations, 700 volunteer liaisons, spanning to support a population of 20,000 congregants. Congregants enroll at their churches. If admitted to the hospital enrolled congregants are identified by the hospital as participants of CHN, and a health navigator is assigned to the participant. With the health navigator, participants design their care plans, and the health navigator coordinates their post-discharge services and transition with a volunteer liaison. The Memphis model is successful for multiple reasons including sharing of medical information through technology, partnering with already established community groups, development of a strong advisory committee, honoring the wisdom and intelligence of liaisons embedded in churches, building trust and shared commitment. To establish long-term social change, training of over 4,000 community members and other benefits from the health system for liaison and clergy members were provided.

3. Engaged and empowered community leadership, networks, and resources faith-based, Area Agencies on Aging, and other community-based organizations (see "Alameda model" below).

Using these three foundational components, C-TAC is developing a best-practice Community Action Project framework with partners from across the country in Alameda County, CA; San Diego, CA; Detroit, MI; Washington, DC; New York City; Providence, Rhode Island; and elsewhere.

Alameda County Case Study

In April 2013, at the request of its members -- including members of the faith community, health systems, and a foundation -- C-TAC initiated work with Allen Temple Baptist church in Alameda County, CA, to develop a first-of-its-kind community and health systems coalition, focused on improving advanced illness care for patients and family caregivers.

Alameda communities, which include Oakland, often collaborate on health and social issues, however, the community and faith-based organizations had never met together on the needs, and challenges in supporting persons with advanced illness and their family caregivers.

Thus, a Consultation was held in November of 2013, including 60 participants, representing places of worship and community stakeholders with a constituency base of over 35,000 people in Alameda County. Its purpose was to ascertain the concerns, needs and resources of the community. The stakeholders agreed an initiative designed to assist those in need of care and their caregivers would benefit the community. The day-long working session resulted in the development of a strategic plan and the formation of the Alameda County Care Alliance (ACCA). The ACCA organization consists presently of the following organizations: Allen Temple Baptist, Glad Tidings, Center of Hope Community Church, Greater St. John Baptist Church, Family Bible Fellowship), other community organizations (Asian Health Services, Catholic Ecumenical Council). The Executive Director, an Allen Temple leader and health professional, has worked from the outset with both CTAC and the leaders of Alameda community to build the ACCA coalition and strengthen the collaborative amongst all stakeholders.

The goals of this community faith-based model are to (1) extend and strengthen the health care delivery system, (2) improve the outcomes for people with advanced illness, (3) reduce the caregiver burden, and (4) strengthen the community support infrastructure to meet the demand for advanced illness care.

The model is designed to be community-based and community-led; toward these ends, the model adheres to the following Community Action Project principles:

1. The starting point is based on relationships with effective community convening organizations such as faith-based organizations or senior centers.
2. It works from the inside-out rather than the outside-in. Its starting point is with the community, and the community's needs and resources, and goes from there to collaborate with health care institutions and other stakeholders at the regional and national level.
3. It is organized based on consensus, with full community participation at all levels.
4. It is focused on building long-term capacity and developing community leadership.

ACCA is a diverse faith and community coalition that is committed to providing community access, a volunteer base, meeting space and other in-kind contributions, in working with health system partners. The model has the following components:

- Identification of patients and family caregivers facing advanced chronic illness in the congregation and other community hubs.
- Technical assistance to train faith leaders and empower them to provide decision-support for patients and families.
- Group-based support and coaching sessions in the church setting.
- Proactive phone calls and in-person visits by dedicated community care navigators following the Coleman Care Transition Coaching template (which contains a patient discharge preparation checklist identifying tasks that should be completed before the patient is discharged from the hospital) with emphasis on advanced illness issues (e.g., advance care planning, management of symptoms and other medical issues, self-care, etc.).

Next Steps with the Community Action Project

We have already learned a great deal from the Alameda County pilot and other Community Action Projects from across the country. So far, the data collected from working among providers, community leaders and family caregivers reveal that:

1. Stakeholders and communities do share common objectives such as keeping patients out of the Emergency Department and ensuring informed and shared decision-making among clinicians, trusted advisors (clergy), families, and patients.
2. Community members (churches, family caregivers, et al.) need to develop the capacity to provide care that meets these shared objectives.

3. "Capacity" for implementing an advanced care program in Oakland (and elsewhere, as we've discovered) was defined as: working relationships between community members and between these organizations and stakeholder groups (e.g., health systems); appropriate training; and community-based personnel to organize, coordinate, and serve as a liaison with stakeholders.

The Community Action model is designed to be community-based and community-led, replicable and sustainable across sites, populations served and community needs and resources. In dialogues with C-TAC members, we've found that the goals and design of this model are amenable to multiple stakeholders (healthcare systems, health plans, Centers for Medicare and Medicaid Services (CMS)) across the country. As part of the 2015 Summit, C-TAC launched a national learning network of community and health system partners to develop scalable and sustainable Community Action models across the country.

Conclusion

The faith community plays a vital role in the lives of people who need advanced care and the loved ones who support them, contributing to both their quality and dignity of life. As we have seen from our work in Alameda County, California, and elsewhere throughout the country, when clergy work in collaboration with the health care delivery team and bring their community resources as part of the care team, the patient, the family and caregivers experience improved shared and informed decision-making, better person- and family-centered care, and a more holistic approach to care.

By including spirituality and a person's belief system into the medical treatment model of advanced illness care, we can transform advanced illness care from a disease-oriented system into a human-relational system that recognizes that while a cure for one's disease may be beyond reach, it is possible to heal.

At C-TAC, we share a common vision that people needing advanced illness care, especially the sickest and the most vulnerable, will receive the medical and spiritual care that matches their needs, values and goals and honors their dignity. Spiritual care is an integral part of the path forward. It offers a pathway of hope—hope for reconciliation, hope for acceptance, and hope that one's final chapter is a story of peace, meaning and love, not a story of pain, isolation and exile.

CHAPTER 4
The Role of Employers:
Taking a Proactive Approach
J. Brent Pawlecki, MD, MMM
and Pamela Kalen

"There's no such thing as work-life balance. There are work-life choices, and you make them, and they have consequences."
—Jack Welch

Sandy works in the Human Resources department of a large global company. She has two college-age children, and her 82-year-old mother, who suffers from dementia, lives with her. While working at her desk each day, Sandy receives phone call after phone call—often ten or more in a day—from her mother. Sandy spends a significant portion of each day responding to her mother's numerous daily-life concerns and questions, often repeating the same conversation many times in one day because her mother does not realize that a similar conversation had occurred only hours earlier. Though Sandy has been able to keep up with the demands of her job and of her mother's care as the dementia worsens and her health continues to decline, Sandy is exhausted and unsure how to keep it all going.

Stories like Sandy's are happening every day—many times a day—all over the country. An employee discovers that a loved one has suddenly become ill and needs to be cared for, or a loved one suffering from multiple chronic diseases continues to need more care over time, or as is the case with Sandy, dementia sets in and a loved one's health and well-being spirals downward. In all cases, the employee finds himself or herself in a difficult situation—trying to balance his or her own household duties and workplace responsibilities and taking care of a sick loved one—all at the same time. The declining physical and emotional state of the loved one not only affects the employee's energy and creative enthusiasm, but also has a ripple effect that transcends much farther – affecting families and the workplace more than most realize.

Employers are already affected by these issues—whether they realize it or not. There is an 8 percent differential in increased health care costs between caregiving and non-caregiving employees, potentially costing U.S. employers an extra estimated $13.4 billion per year.[37] Not only are they facing a financial impact in terms of productivity loss, but they also are experiencing the adverse health effects on their own employees as a result of caregiving and bereavement.

As a result, employers face an urgent need to educate their workforce on advanced illness and to adopt effective policies and practices to help them and their employees deal with it. Advanced illness and the related concerns are complex and multifaceted. Longer life expectancy, an aging workforce, and technological advancements in medical care that keep people with serious illnesses alive and more productive longer, mean that employers have a stake in caregiving and its ramifications. Therefore, employers must become involved in understanding the issues and responding to the challenges.

Consider the U.S. demographics today. The National Hospice and Palliative Care Organization estimates that by the year 2050, the number of adults aged 65 or older will reach 87 million.[38] As the population is aging (see Chapter 1), the workforce is also aging. In 1992, workers 55 and older made up less than 12 percent of the workforce. By 2012, they were about 21 percent. And by 2022, they are projected to be over 25 percent of the total workforce.[39] More and more people are choosing to remain in the workforce longer, or to return in some capacity after having retired. For some, this is a choice; for others a necessity. A report by Bloomberg

News found that U.S. employees old enough to retire now outnumber teenagers in the workforce for the first time since 1948.[40] And, according to research conducted by AARP, almost half of all employees aged 45-70 envision working into their 70s and beyond.[41]

As the baby boomers age and reach older adulthood, not only will a larger proportion of this population still be in the workplace, they also will assume another role—caregivers for their parents, spouses and relatives while facing their own advanced illness issues. Likewise, as the boomers age, their children—today's younger workers—will also take on greater responsibilities as family caregivers.

More than 80 percent of long-term care services in the U.S., (including services for advanced illness), are provided by family caregivers,[42], and more than 73 percent of those caregivers were still employed while caring for a family member.[43]

Further data indicate that the percentage of adults with the dual role of caregiver/employee rose from 62 percent in 2005 to 69 percent in 2009. Research indicated that many of these employees had to arrive at work late, leave early or take time off during the day to provide the care, an increase from 57 percent in 2004 to 65 percent in 2009.[44]

These studies point to definitive *economic* and *emotional* outcomes for both employees and employers as a result of employees' health-related and caregiving issues. A recent internal survey done by a Fortune 500 company revealed that of current caregivers, one in five is actively considering leaving the workforce to deal with their caregiving responsibilities. That is a lot of resources, investment in training, and historical knowledge that might be lost as a result of this issue.

With an aging workforce and an increasing number of long-term caregivers, how does the workplace deal with this growing trend? How do employers address these issues for their workforce? What can be done to lessen the emotional and economic impact on both employees and employers?

Emotional Impact on Employee

Emotional issues are difficult to quantify, yet they are often the most visible reactions to any situation. Each individual handles stress and difficult situations differently. However, employees who are affected by the onset of caring for loved ones with advanced illness tend to demonstrate some common behaviors.

1. Initially, the employee may slog through silently, not sharing with his supervisor or coworkers, trying to keep up with the demands. It may work for a time, but performance slacks.
2. While trying to hide the situation from others, the employee's behavior may be negatively perceived by his coworkers and supervisor as being indifferent, lacking concentration or not performing the necessary job functions. If identified earlier, perhaps an alternative work arrangement could have been worked out, keeping the employee's work reputation intact.

> *The National Business Group on Health reports increased stress levels (four or five on a five-point scale) to 63 percent of caregivers.*

Depression is another adverse effect of caregiving. According to the American Academy of Family Physicians, depression is the most common health problem among caregivers. One study revealed that anxiety was present in 17.5 percent of caregivers,[45] and further data showed that family caregivers who provided care 36 or more hours a week were more likely to experience symptoms of depression or anxiety. When caring for a spouse, the rate was six times higher; when caring for a parent, it was twice as high.[46]

In addition to the employee, the spouse, significant other, partner or other dependents and family members are often affected by the care that is given to the sick loved one. Caregivers often forego their own health and well-being, delaying needed care, skipping exercise and eating on the run.

Emotional Impact on Employer

There is also an *emotional* impact on the management of the company and the coworkers of the employee. Just as it is difficult to quantify the emotional impact on the employee, the same is true for the employer, and it can be more widespread than is known. For example:

1. Co-workers may be called upon to take on additional work when the affected employee is on leave, takes intermittent time off for treatment or caregiving responsibilities, or has a loss of productivity when not feeling well or distracted by worries and outside responsibilities.

2. Co-workers may be concerned about their colleague's health or stress if they are aware of the situation. If co-workers are unaware, they may be resentful of their colleague's absences and lack of productivity.

3. Supervisors need guidance on how to find the right balance of being supportive and not taking on too much responsibility outside the scope of appropriate work relationship.

4. Employers should make sure that supervisors are offered support from Human Resources (HR), Employee Assistance Programs (EAP), or other sources to help them manage difficult situations.

In addition, employers must consider how to work around the following challenges:

- Does the employee continue to work without adjusting his/her schedule yet is still cognizant of the demands of the job?
- Does the employee work in an environment that allows flexibility, i.e., working from home?
- Does the employee ignore existing standards by redefining the standard operating procedures and designing his or her own?

Economic Impact to Employee

The economic impact can be just as traumatic as the emotional impact. Some of the predicted patterns that employees might exhibit when faced with an advanced illness issue include:

1. Taking time away from work to manage appointments and caregiving responsibilities.
2. Changing their status from full-time to part-time work to manage their caregiving responsibilities.
3. Foregoing promotions or transfers because of inability to take on more responsibility at work or need to stay closer to those for whom they are providing care.
4. Resigning from work or taking a leave of absence.

The choices employees make as they juggle their work responsibilities with their caregiving responsibilities have a ripple effect throughout the organization and could ultimately affect the company's bottom line.

Economic Impact to Employer

Employers know that their company won't be successful without healthy and productive employees. With the aging of the population and many people choosing to work beyond the traditional retirement age, employers are facing an older workforce with more associated health problems and increasing costs for health and disability benefits. Additionally, more of their employees, regardless of age, will face increasing caregiving responsibilities that will require more of their attention.

The *economic* impact on the employer is complex and poses several challenges.

As stated previously, there is an 8 percent differential in increased health care costs between caregiving and non-caregiving employees, potentially costing U.S. employers an extra estimated $13.4 billion per year.[47] Furthermore, the estimated cost to employers ranges from $17.1 billion to $33.6 billion annually attributable to caregiving.[48] These costs are due to absenteeism ($5.1 billion), shifts from full-time to part-time work ($4.8 billion), replacing employees ($6.6 billion), and workday interruptions ($6.3 billion).[49] There is also a cost to employers if they have to recruit, hire and train a new employee if an employee caregiver has to leave the workforce.

The value of the services family caregivers (i.e., employees) provide for "free" is estimated to be $450 billion a year. That is more than twice the total paid for long-term services and supports regardless of the payer source ($203 billion in 2009).[50] The total estimated cost to employers for all full-time employed caregivers is a staggering $33.6 billion. The average costs per employee for caregiving responsibilities ranges from $2,100 to $2,400.[51]

In addition, employers also face the following challenges:

1. Reduced productivity and loss of valued expertise due to employee's health-related absences, disability leave, early retirement or premature death.

2. Increase in absenteeism and presenteeism when an employee is caring for a loved one with a serious or chronic illness.

3. The Family Medical Leave Act (FMLA) is designed to help employees balance their work and family responsibilities. Because FMLA is non-paid, the employee suffers lost income and the employer loses the employee's contributions to the workplace.

Developing a Plan

Addressing issues related to advanced illness in the workplace is a complex process that will vary from organization to organization depending on the make-up of the workforce. Nevertheless, organizations share a common goal of promoting the best-practice delivery of health care, while empowering individuals to make informed choices for themselves and their family members, thus limiting the distractions that interfere with their overall well-being and the productivity in their work.

Each year, as millions of employees struggle to navigate between caring for their ill loved ones, their household duties and their workplace responsibilities, more and more employers are finding it beneficial to take positive steps toward supporting their employee caregivers through advanced illness planning, individual care planning, and grief and bereavement.

Several Fortune 500 companies, including The Goodyear Tire and Rubber Company, General Electric, IBM, Pitney Bowes and PepsiCo, have worked independently and with each other through the National Business Group on Health to specifically address advanced illness issues for their employees. These companies have begun to implement policies and create educational tools, family planning guides, and support programs to assist their employees facing advanced illness.

They have found that by initiating conversations with top management and reviewing available data about the employee population and the available benefits, they have been able to identify opportunities to invest in the health of the workforce and to play a key role in supporting employees and their dependents who are dealing with advanced illness.

The first step in developing a plan is to assess and survey the staff and what current resources are available to the employer and employee both inside and outside of the company. A collective brainstorming session might be in order to begin the thought and planning process.

A large national retail company, for example, has identified eldercare as the fastest growing work-family challenge to emerge in the past decade. They have found that approximately 17 percent of their workforce has family caregiving responsibilities for an elder relative. Twenty percent of these report their health status as fair or poor – leading to higher health care costs.

As a result of these findings, the company has developed a set of benefits for caregivers including up to 10 days paid sick leave to provide caregiving services, allowing supervisors to make flex time available on an individual basis, and allowing up to 12 weeks Family Medical Leave Act/Leave of Absence (FMLA/LOA) for certain employees to help care for a family member. The company also provides EAP services and offers an on-site ElderCare Support Group to provide monthly support and immediate crisis help for those who are caring for older adults.

The pharmaceutical giant, Pfizer, has found that their caregiver employees do not want sick days. Instead, they would prefer to have flexible time and the ability to work virtually if they need to attend a doctor's appointment with their loved one. As a member of ReACT (Respect A Caregivers Time), a coalition of 30 companies that covers almost 1 million workers across the country and is committed to engaging caregiver employees in the workplace, Pfizer has realized that hiring and training a new employee to replace a caregiver who had to leave his or her job is often more expensive than working with the caregiver's schedule. So, working with their caregiver employees to find mutually agreeable accommodations has paid off both economically for the company and emotionally for the employees. They have also found that change is most successful when the desire and drive for that change comes from the top of the organization, especially the CEO. When that willingness to make change exists, it can pay huge dividends in the long run.

The point is that most people have been touched by advanced illness in some way and understand the importance of providing a supportive work environment and benefits. By leveraging leadership support at all levels in the organization, management can create a supportive work environment by implementing a variety of policies and programs that help employees deal with their own or a loved one's illness. Examples include:

- Allowing workplace accommodations including flexible hours, working from home, and modification of work duties.
- Developing or identifying existing materials that educate employees about issues related to care during an advanced illness.

Resources are available from the *National Healthcare Decisions Day*, *Engage with Grace*, and *The Conversation Project*.

- Including questions in the organization's health assessment about advance illness preparation and caregiving issues. Asking employees if they are in a caregiving role or if they have an advance directive or other document that spells out their preferences for their own medical care.
- Developing learning tools that encompass planning for the future, incorporating significant life events such as pregnancy, 401(K), education and retirement.

Focusing on bottom-line issues—data that support a definitive financial impact—will enhance the employer's efforts to create a supportive work environment. This should begin with a review of the organization's health claims data that specifically quantifies the financial and workplace impact of advanced illness care issues. Data will likely be available for some or all of these areas: bereavement leave; Consolidated Omnibus Budget Reconciliation Act (COBRA) usage; Employee Assistance Programs (EAPs); Family Medical Leave Act (FMLA) usage; Flex-time arrangements; insurance (long-term care and short- and long-term disability; and local medical plan partner information such as premiums, participation, etc.).

While assessing employee needs and concerns is an important first step in creating a supporting environment for dealing with advanced illness, it is also important to raise awareness and educate employees and other stakeholders about caregiving issues and their impact on the workplace. Many companies and health care organizations are already doing this. It is important to utilize whatever is already available. Preparation is key. A well-formed wellness plan involving a health crisis communication element will enable employers and employees alike to prepare themselves for advanced illness cases that will inevitably rise throughout life.

Goodyear, a large global tire manufacturing company, has built an awareness campaign as "planning for the future" within its U.S. wellness programs. On its internal wellness site are tools to assist with advance directives, documentation of financial accounts and information to help individuals consider the best choices for themselves should something bad happen with their health. Its communications around this topic coincide with the national campaign of the National Healthcare Decisions Day and The Conversation Project.

Even without the benefit of external resources, employers can craft a wellness road map focusing on advanced illness issues. Here are some points to consider:

1. Share as much information as possible with employees on the importance of having a plan or an advance directive by disseminating this information via the company newsletter, intranet sites, bulletin boards, presentations and any and all media available for communication.
2. Survey the workforce with a health assessment, and include questions that address advanced illness and other caregiving issues.
3. Consider asking case management vendors to ask employees and their dependents if they have living wills.
4. Design programs to mitigate costs. Start with a brainstorming session within the organization in which the focus is on wellness and advanced illness concerns.
5. Continue to research and evaluate the impact of existing cases within the company – both from an economic and emotional side. This includes reviewing an employee's increased amount of time spent on caregiving.
6. Implement a training program for management dealing with the coping of the "new" health care issues.

Recommendations of the National Business Group on Health
For Developing an Advanced Illness Care Plan

1. Identify key stakeholders and obtain buy-in

Present the business case to senior management, built on the foundation of the data and information you have reviewed for advanced illness and palliative care planning and policies.

2. Assess employee needs and concerns

a. Perform employee needs assessment through workgroups and employee satisfaction surveys and by obtaining general feedback.

b. Include questions in your work/life questionnaire about advanced illness and palliative care, as well as planning for the future.

c. As part of your health assessment or work/life questionnaire, ask employees if they are in a caregiving role for a family member or friend. Family caregivers are more likely than non-caregivers to experience symptoms of depression or anxiety and are more likely to defer preventive health screenings.

3. Decide who will be responsible for ensuring that the following tasks are accomplished:

a. Reviewing coverage under both medical and prescription plans to determine if there are any gaps in palliative and hospice care.

b. Assessing support programs, gap analysis and resources for advanced illness planning that might be available through EAP or other vendors.

c. Determining the communications needs for both managers and employees and developing an appropriate communications plan for them and other key audiences.

4. Assess your company's resources, demographics and culture to ensure that the approach best fits the needs of your organization.

Sharing Experiences

Once the plan is in place, management must communicate the new company guidelines to all stakeholders via all forms of available media, including social media. These are sensitive topics and, as such, are inherently difficult issues for all involved. Provide information that is accurate, simple and easy to understand.

The three primary stakeholders are the employees (including the people for whom they may be administering advanced care, dependents, families and loved ones), employers (including direct management, as well as co-workers) and vendors (those who supply the caregivers products or services via company-supported financing or external sources).

The following checklist, developed by the National Business Group on Health, offers helpful guidelines for sharing information with various stakeholders[52]:

National Business Group on Health

Checklist for Sharing Policies and Practices on

Advanced Illness Care

Employees

1. Develop materials that educate employees about issues related to care during an advanced illness. The materials should include information on the following issues:

    - Assistance in developing or learning about health care proxies (a document that allows a patient to appoint an agent to make health care decisions in the event that the primary individual is incapable of executing such decisions).

    - Advance directives, including guidelines for your particular state.

    - Medical orders for life-sustaining treatment (MOLST).

    - Physician's orders for life-sustaining treatment (POLST).

    - Family and Medical Leave Act (FMLA) benefits.

    - Consolidated Omnibus Budget Reconciliation Act (COBRA) benefits.

    - Employee resources that are available from vendors, such as employee assistance programs (EAPs), bereavement counseling and support groups.

---

2. After employees have an understanding of the benefits offered, give them a list of resources, and teach them on how to access other resources available within

your organization. Specifically, employees should be kept informed about the following:

- Employee assistance programs (EAPs).
- The appropriate contact person for FMLA, COBRA and other employee benefits.
- Bereavement counseling and any other behavioral health resources, including those for ill or bereaved co-workers.
- Health plan resources, including coverage of palliative, hospice and advanced illness (i.e., end-of-life) care.

3. Include in key communications the legal resources (internally, if available) employees can access for drafting advance directives and estate planning documents. Also encourage financial counseling to ensure fiscal stability for both the patient and family.

4. Advise employees what resources are available for dependents or others covered by company plans. This can be done by communicating eligibility criteria for receiving benefits from several programs. Ensure that the material communicated is simple and easy to understand, minus jargon and acronyms.

5. Develop a feedback process to gauge satisfaction levels from employees and other stakeholders.

Employers

Groups within a company traditionally meet to discuss business issues. Consider discussing issues dealing with wellness, health and advanced illness issues. If this is not possible, consider separate meetings to specifically discuss with managers ways to support employees who have or are confronted with advanced illness issues.

Vendors

Some key topics to discuss with vendors might include:

1. Eligibility criteria for coverage under health and pharmaceutical plans.
2. Transparency of referral network.
3. Availability of palliative care resources.

Challenges and Opportunities

While several companies have made progress in implementing advanced illness programs in the workplace to assist employees who are sick and those who are caregivers, there remain skeptics, and minimal hard evidence exists that proves the overall value of such programs. This is both a challenge and an opportunity. Several studies have confirmed the value of palliative care (with an average cost decrease of 45 percent): enrolled patients required fewer emergency room and hospital admissions and lower use of intensive care units, and they expressed greater satisfaction with their care when compared to usual-care patients.[53] While this can benefit both patients and caregivers, careful data collection of employer health plans is needed to properly demonstrate the value that these interventions can provide.

Despite the lack of solid metrics that justify the efforts, some employers are implementing programs, and they should continue to use these occasions to demonstrate to employees the importance of such efforts. After all, history has shown us that employers intuitively accepted the value of weight-loss programs long before definitive data became available proving such.

Employers must also address the fear that some employees have about discussing their personal problems and extra-occupational activities outside the workplace. The fear is magnified at a time when they won't be at peak performance. They may also worry that they could be targeted for downsizing. Companies and management need to be encouraged to support such intangible compassionate, moral and ethical issues that allay employee fears and foster a healthy and viable workplace.

All plans begin with a thoughtful dialog, and we should not presume that the start of an initiative would automatically begin with the employer. While all parties involved have a lot to gain from a proactive approach to advanced illness, there should be a dual commitment to finding solutions to an issue. There are many support groups that can assist in this process, however, someone has to take the lead, but that should not preclude anyone involved from "doing some homework."

Employers can do their part by initiating or increasing focused data collection regarding end-of-life issues impacting their own organizations. At the same time, they should proactively seek out employees involved with end-of-life issues.

For employees, it's important to stay healthy. The case for maintaining a healthy lifestyle cannot be overstated. Staying active, eating a healthy diet, getting sufficient sleep and keeping up with doctors' appointments, screening medications, etc., are all proactive approaches to good health. The good habits also will be an ally when and if you have to become a caregiver.

Employees should also conduct a "self-survey." Using the counsel of individuals and groups within and outside of the company, they should develop their own written "health care" plan and share it with others, especially family and loved ones. At the same time, they should develop a list of resources – available through the Internet, local or company library and a variety of other sources, and seek emotional support when they need it. Employees should not hesitate to talk to their employers (manager or human resources group) or health care professional about their situation. There are many sources for these types of services. They need to become aware of their limitations, take periodic breaks, and re-charge their living battery. And finally, they should participate in workplace planning and initiatives to help themselves and their colleagues as their employers seek ways to help employee caregivers.

C-TAC created an Employer Committee to empower employers to take positive steps toward supporting employees on all levels including caregiving responsibilities, advanced illness planning and individual care planning, advanced illness and grief and bereavement. They have found that the single most powerful intervention for employers is training for supervisors to help employed caregivers to balance work and caregiving. They also have created a checklist that identifies specific action items employers can take to assist employee caregivers. These are grouped into four categories—informal resources, individual care planning, administrative support, and evaluation and metrics— and can be found at thectac.org.

As the population and the workforce continue to age, and the number of employee caregivers increases, advanced illness will have an even greater emotional and economic impact on both employees and employers. Jack Welch was right: people make work-life choices, and those choices have consequences for both employees and employers. Throughout this chapter, we have attempted to show that there is a path forward where employees and employers can work together to help each other cope better and lessen the impact of advanced illness by instituting policies and programs to support employee caregivers and help them make difficult work-life choices.

Employers cannot erase the tremendous challenges that employees face as caregivers following a health crisis. They can, however, recognize the impact on their business or organization and the strains that their employees face, and they can foster the important discussions necessary with plans and tools that will help ease this burden.

CHAPTER 5

Best Practice Care Delivery Models

Bud Hammes, PhD, Randall Krakauer, MD, and Brad Stuart, MD

"The future is already here – it's just not evenly distributed."
—William Gibson

Despite the gaps that exist between the type and quality of care people with advanced illness receive and what they want and expect to receive, several providers have made significant strides in closing that gap and are providing high-quality advanced illness care. Indeed, innovative and proven models of care for advanced illness are ready for scaling and dissemination. Data shows these new care management practices relieve suffering, maximize personal choice and reduce unnecessary hospitalization and avoidable costs.[54] Yet, they have been slow to spread. If evidence like this had been developed for a new drug, it would now be a mainstay of treatment. Proven practices in advanced illness, however, have not yet been widely implemented.

The reasons for this are many. Transforming care is harder than just writing a prescription. Real transformation requires structural changes in the delivery system, which takes investment of time and money, as well as willingness to change. Reform will disrupt traditional health care as the system moves away from fee-for-service (FFS) toward accepting risk and expands beyond care of individuals toward managing the health of populations. New care models for advanced illness are helping to lead these changes, and are confronting important challenges along the way.

Because fee-for-service pays providers a fee for each service they perform, it gives providers an incentive to provide more services. This can lead to overuse of services and unnecessary care in all stages of disease, and advanced illness is no exception. But reimbursement reform alone is not enough. Financial incentives are already favorably aligned toward care management innovation in Medicare Advantage (MA) plans, Accountable Care Organizations (ACOs), Patient-Centered Medical Homes (PCMHs) and other new settings. Despite the favorable business case, however, most of these entities have not yet developed advanced care interventions that significantly improve quality and access or that are replicable, scalable and sustainable. Change is hard, and it must be led by early adopters who want to be out front in the new world of American healthcare.

This chapter describes models of care for advanced illness that work. They focus on people, not just patients. They provide education and coaching so people with advanced illness, their families and caregivers can make truly informed choices about their care in partnership with their care teams and their physicians. When this is done well, the care they receive is truly transformed. It changes from treatment of illness provided mostly in the hospital to real health care that is brought to them where they live with real impact on their lives and the lives of loved ones. This care is more affordable, because it prevents costly hospital stays that such seriously ill people would not elect if given a choice.

Although transforming care for advanced illness requires investment, the payoffs are clear and in complete alignment with increasing quality and access. Advanced care is truly person-centered. Where it is implemented properly, physicians, hospitals and other providers are drawn together through real-time communication to create an integrated system with care coordination. A valuable byproduct of this human process is the potential for a significant reduction in the cost of care. No other care innovation has the capacity to achieve such high returns in terms of quality and cost, particularly for Medicare. Indeed, our current investment in avoidable and counterproductive care in advanced Illness represents an inappropriate distribution of scarce medical resources away from areas of greater need and potential.

Care Management of Advanced Illness

People in the early stages of chronic illnesses like diabetes or COPD are quite capable of managing their own care. Visits to primary care physicians (PCPs) and specialists are not hard to coordinate. But illness often becomes more serious, or advanced, and care becomes more complex just as capacity for self-management declines. Visits to the emergency room (ER) and hospital stays become more frequent. At the same time, confusion, depression and other problems make it harder to juggle appointments, lab tests and medications.

Providing supportive care management to selected people with advanced illness makes sense, not just for these individuals, but for the healthcare system and society. Bringing care to people where they live, through nursing visits and by phone, helps seriously ill people cope and adapt. Their doctors know how they're doing even if they can't make it into the office. Problems are solved before they reach a crisis point, so emergencies are prevented and unnecessary hospital admissions are avoided.

Providing care management to the most seriously ill is feasible and affordable, and it benefits the whole population. Half of all health care costs are incurred by only five percent of Americans, so improving care for that segment pays off in terms of overall outcomes and costs. Focusing on that five percent changes the game for everyone.

Care management is defined as providing expert and experienced advice and assistance to people with advanced illness in order to help with informed decision making, support families and caregivers, and ensure independent living for as long as possible. This care management process needs to be integrated seamlessly into regular medical care. When this is done properly, physicians are supported as well. They get timely reports about the people they worry about the most, and care teams become their eyes, ears and hands in the home and community. Providing such expert assistance is of high value to physicians, particularly when demands on their time can be overwhelming.

Overarching Principles of Advanced Care

Care management for advanced illness can be structured in many ways—but however it is provided, advanced care needs to follow a number of important principles in order to be effective. If any of these are lacking, clinical and financial outcomes may not be as good as they could be. This can threaten the sustainability of new programs.

Model advanced care interventions pay close attention to the following tasks:

1. *Population definition and selection.* The population with advanced illness needs to be described accurately so clinicians know which of their patients are appropriate for care management. Outcomes are optimal when programs focus mainly on people who are seriously ill. As information technology advances, people will be selected automatically for advanced care so they do not have to wait to be referred.

2. *Personal goals drive care, not just clinical needs.* Everyone, no matter how ill, wants certain things above all others. For many, these personal goals are simple and straightforward: staying independent, being with family, being at peace with themselves and their faith, and living in safety and comfort. Advanced care teams seek to understand these goals and craft care plans that help achieve them. This boosts motivation for self-care, adherence to medications, and other factors that stabilize health.

3. *System-integrating care management.* A well-designed and well-executed advanced care program doesn't just coordinate care—it integrates care settings to create a true system of care. Inpatient clinicians, including hospitalists and palliative care teams are connected in real time with physicians in their offices and teams providing care at home. Care teams are closely supervised and directed by the physicians who are in charge of the person's care, supplemented by consultation from trained medical directors.

4. *Advance care planning occurs at the person's own pace.* Advance care planning is critical; if it doesn't happen, care defaults to emergency hospital treatment. Ideally, advance care planning is community-based, starting before people even become ill. But the most important stages occur when illness becomes advanced. All too often, discussions are started late in the course of illness in hospital or doctor's office, too late, or not at all. Advanced care teams ensure that critical conversations happen continuously in the safety and comfort of home at a relaxed pace. This assures true shared decision-making.

5. *Customized, evolving mix of curative and palliative care.* Almost everyone starts out wanting their disease to be controlled, whatever it takes. It's only when the burdens of treatment begin to outweigh the benefits that people start to consider options other than full-bore curative treatment. As preferences for care naturally evolve, care itself needs to evolve in parallel. Advanced care provides treatment at home, such as intravenous antibiotics, but phases in less aggressive and more comfort-oriented care in concert with personal wishes.

6. *Leverage systemic structural innovation.* As data are reported on early experiments with ACOs and PCMHs, it is becoming clear that outcomes vary across systems. Best practices are emerging, and many of them embody principles of advanced care. Targeting

seriously ill patients for intervention and physician-directed teams are only two examples. As the next phase of health care reform gets underway, advanced care is well positioned to help lead the development of new infrastructure and care processes.

7. *Constructive messaging and engagement.* For too long, progress in improving care for people with advanced illness has been held back by fears associated with the end of life. Clinicians who have waited for signs of death to refer their patients to hospice and palliative care have found it easier to use advanced care interventions. Careful attention to audience-specific messaging leads to high levels of acceptance by people with advanced illness, their families and physicians.

Models That Work

Thanks to the foresight, commitment and inventiveness of many advanced care pioneers across the country, we are beginning to see the value these principles provide to patients and their families, providers and health plans. The examples that follow highlight advanced illness care models that work by providing high quality, person-centered care delivered in the appropriate setting at the right time. The challenge is to apply these models on a larger scale so people everywhere can get the care they want, expect and deserve.

Aetna Compassionate Care

Aetna Compassionate Care has been in place for nearly ten years. Aetna case managers with training and experience in advanced illness reach out to physicians and members to provide support and assistance and to facilitate informed decisions, pain relief and other identified needs.

In the Medicare Advantage population, approximately one percent of members are engaged in this program annually—and it is very favorably received by participating physicians and especially by member/patients and families.

For those in the program the results speak for themselves: 82 percent have elected hospice, days of acute care have been reduced by 82 percent, the number of days spent in ICU have been reduced by 86 percent, members (on average) have saved $12,900, and members report a very high level of satisfaction.

Aetna's program allows for commercially insured members to receive concurrent "curative" therapy with an anticipated survival of 12 months. This has not resulted in an increase in cost when provided in conjunction with Compassionate Care Case management. Dr. Randall Krakauer, Vice President and National Medical Director for Medical Strategy indicates Aetna is so satisfied with the results of the program that enhancements are planned. According to Dr. Krakauer, "particularly for Medicare— if we seek favorable impact at the intersection of quality and cost—this is the 'mother load.' Acceptance of ones' mortality is a process, not an epiphany, and it is past-time for patient support such as this to become 'standard of care.'"

Respecting Choices® (RC)— Gundersen Health System's advance care planning program

The Gundersen Health System has been focused on improving person and family centered care and the promotion of shared decision-making since the mid 80's by learning how to implement effective advance care planning practices as a routine of care. This work has resulted in a nationally and internationally recognized and implemented program that helps patients of all ages and illness, especially those with advanced illness, to plan for future anticipated health care decisions. The RC approach relies on four critical, interconnected elements:

1. Delivery system redesign;
2. The creation and training of advance care planning facilitators and a team approach;
3. Community and patient engagement; and
4. Continuous quality improvement of elements 1-3.[55]

One of the powerful components of the RC approach is its attention to assisting patients and families to reflect on, clarify, and articulate their values, goals, and preferences about health care. It is often assumed that what patients mostly need in making plans for future health care decisions is information either about treatments or their legal rights. While such information is important to different degrees for different patients, this information cannot be really evaluated by patients until these patients first are clear what most matters to them. To clarify such values and priorities, the RC model trains non-physicians to learn how to guide people and those closest to them through a reflective process. This process is done in stages so that individuals can more realistically plan at different stages of health: e.g., when they are relatively healthy (First Steps®); when they have an advanced illness and suffering serious complications (Next Steps); and when they have an end-stage illness and a short life expectancy (Last Steps®).

The RC achieves its effectiveness through standardization of system and process across settings of care and in it reliable training methods.[56] This has allowed this approach to be scaled to large populations, like in Honoring Choices Minnesota and Wisconsin, and to large health systems, like Kaiser Permanente in Northern California.[57] It has also shown to be effective in knowing and honoring preferences in diverse populations. This approach to advance care planning helps realize all seven overarching principles of advanced care described above and helps improve the delivery of primary palliative care.

Allina Health LifeCourse ™

In 2012 Allina Health, a large health system in the Midwest, began researching an approach to whole person care for individuals and families living with serious illness in its later stages. LifeCourse provides a layer of support that complements primary and acute care, traditional home based services, and care management.

LifeCourse supports individuals along their illness trajectory to articulate goals and make decisions based on what matters most to them. This approach aligns with the principles of advanced care by helping people plan at their own pace and customize their care to best meet their goals and wishes. Participants receive a monthly visit from a lay healthcare worker, called a care guide, who acts as a primary contact as the patient moves across settings.

Care guides:
- Deliver whole person care through structured question sets, assessments and activities aligning with an expanded set of palliative care domains and practices.
- Use a family-oriented approach to understand needs, leverage strengths, and empower families to effectively support their loved ones.
- Ask patients and caregivers to articulate individualized goals and take part in decision making.

Early results indicate that individuals and families in LifeCourse are better able to maintain quality of life as compared to a control group receiving usual care. Findings also demonstrate increased completion of advance care planning and access to hospice and palliative care, decreased utilization of services and an overall reduction in total cost of care.

In addition to supporting individuals and their families, LifeCourse promotes public dialogue with community, healthcare and public sectors to support constructive engagement around caring for people later in life. Through a partnership with Twin Cities Public Television our public website is a resource to supporting this dialogue through our documentaries series Late Life: Living with Chronic Illness, patient stories, video clips and consumer resources (www.lifecoursemn.org).[58]

Sutter Health's Advanced Illness Management (AIM) Program

AIM targets the elderly population with chronic conditions in Northern California. The program originated and is centered in Sacramento. AIM attempts to take primary care out of the hospital and into the home for patients with chronic conditions. Recognizing that intense acute care is not what patients with advanced illness need, AIM focuses on care management, treatment and palliation. Sutter started AIM as a system dedicated to avoiding debilitating trips to the hospital. This care often starts in the hospital after a patient who has been admitted is recommended for the program and then transitions into the home. AIM works by assigning each patient a multidisciplinary team to be in charge of their care. Each team is responsible for a caseload of approximately 150 patients. A standard team is made up of roughly 16 people and includes nurses, social workers, physical therapists, and case managers who work in a highly collaborative and coordinated environment, which is underscored by weekly team meetings to discuss patients and problems. The goal is to give patients the consistent low-maintenance care they need at home rather than leaving them to fend for themselves, only stepping in when an emergency occurs. As of 2013, AIM has enrolled nearly one thousand patients and has grown considerably in the six years of its existence.

AIM has seen measureable success over the course of its existence. Internal studies have found that after 90 days of enrollment AIM leads to a 60 percent decrease in hospitalizations, a 63 percent (29 days per case) decrease in intensive-care days, and a 50 percent decrease in physician visits. Also after 90 days post-AIM enrollment, the average Medicare savings are $2,000 per month. However, because of the current limits on Medicare reimbursement (no reimbursement for care coordination and travel expenses), Sutter barely breaks even on the program. In order for AIM to be expanded, Medicare would have to reimburse Sutter for the expenses unique to this program.

Sharp HospiceCare Transitions Program

Sharp HealthCare, a not-for-profit health care delivery system based out of San Diego, California, has found great success with its program, *Transitions*. *Transitions* targets patients suspected of utilizing the hospital as a tool to manage their disease—an unhealthy, expensive pattern for both patient and provider. It addresses the failures in traditional treatment by focusing on four proven "pillars:"

1. In-home medical consultation,
2. Ongoing evidence-based prognostication,
3. Caregiver support, and
4. Advance health care planning.

Within these pillars, *Transitions* employs a variety of techniques that include: increasing family and caregiver education, making prognoses based on the natural progression of the steps of the disease rather than on a calendar, and coordinating and disseminating patient information between members of the physician and caregiver team including monthly meetings.

A two-year study of 155 patients suffering from heart failure enrolled in the program compared their length of stay in the program with the same length of time they spent before entering program. The results were significant:

Other Examples of Hospice Programs Developing Innovative Transition Models include:

Agrace Hospice Care (Madison, WI)

Capital Caring (Falls Church, VA)

Catawba Regional Hospice (Newton, NC)

Chapters Health Systems (Temple Terrace, FL)

Community Hospice of Texas (Fort Worth, TX)

Cornerstone Hospice & Palliative Care (Tavares, FL)

Covenant Hospice (Pensacola, FL)

The Denver Hospice (Denver, CO)

Four Seasons (Flat Rock, NC)

Home & Hospice Care of Rhode Island (Providence, RI)

Hope Healthcare Services (Fort Myers, FL)

HopeHealth (Hyannis, MA)

HopeWest Hospice (Grand Junction, CO)

Hosparus Inc. (Louisville, KY)

Hospice Buffalo (Cheektowaga, NY)

Hospice of Chattanooga (Chattanooga, TN)

Hospice of Michigan (Detroit, MI)

Hospice of the Valley (Phoenix, AZ)

Hospice of the Western Reserve (Cleveland, OH)

Midwest Palliative & Hospice CareCenter (Glenview, IL)

MJHS Hospice and Palliative Care (New York, NY)

Nathan Adelson Hospice (Las Vegas, NV)

Sutter Care at Home (Emeryville, CA)

Trustbridge (West Palm Beach, FL)

Valley Hospice, Inc. (Rayland, OH)

VNSNY Hospice and Palliative Care (New York, NY)

These are a few examples – many similar programs exist across the country.

- The hospitalization rate decreased from 32 percent to 17 percent,
- Emergency department visits decreased from 57 percent to 31 percent, and
- The average total cost decreased from $73,000 to $47,000.

These statistics are particularly impressive given that they defy the natural progression of chronic diseases, which usually leads to increased costs and hospitalizations over time.

Moving *Transitions* to a larger-scale may require some restructuring of reimbursement, but even the conservative estimates in the study show that Transitions has the potential to become a large-scale, financially stable program that can achieve improved health outcomes and lower costs.

UnitedHealth Group Advanced Illness Care Management Program

United's Advanced Illness Care Management Program is focused on members facing life-limiting illness, generally in the last 12-18 months of life. The program uses a predictive model to identify possible candidates by taking into account each member's utilization history, functional status, and clinical and disease-specific data. Each member who enters the program receives a comprehensive care plan based on individual's values and goals (for longevity, function, and comfort) that addresses care coordination, advance care planning, education, and symptom management. This plan is re-visited every 30 days or with any change in condition of the patient. United has found that by developing a detailed plan early in the care continuum, the care team can alleviate some of the anxiety and stress on the patient and the family later on when the patient's condition is deteriorating.

United has found that over 95 percent of those participating in the Advanced Illness Care Management Program (including caregivers) are satisfied with their care, and this has been accompanied by a significant reduction in medical interventions the patient does not want. United attributes part of this success to the fact that over 95 percent of participants in the program have identified their preferred site of death and over 75 percent have a comprehensive advance directive within 120 days of enrollment. Enrollment in hospice has also increased.[59]

Kaiser Permanente Advanced Illness Coordinated Care® (AICC™) Program

This program increases access to specialty trained palliative support, embeds specialists in high-risk settings, systematically addresses care planning, and is developing complex medical homes for the most seriously ill enrollees.

AICC has been tested in three randomized controlled trials and the results have demonstrated improved communication about discomfort, support for decision making and problem resolution, and attention to caregiver needs. AICC participants were also 2.23 times more likely to formulate an advance directive (73 days sooner) and 71 percent died at home, in accordance with their wishes, compared with 51 percent of usual care patients. Furthermore, AICC participants had 1.89 fewer inpatient admissions, were 11 percent less likely to visit the Emergency Department, and the mean cost of care was $7,552 less than for usual care patients.[60]

Positive Impact

Providing expert support to patients with advanced illness and their families represents the greatest opportunity to impact the quality and cost of advanced illness care, particularly for Medicare. These services include: psychosocial support, education and decision support, facilitated pain relief and helping the family cope and come to peace. By providing these services, programs such as those described above and others have achieved changes that can only be described as dramatic. They have tripled the hospice election rate, reduced unnecessary and counterproductive acute care utilization by 60 – 85 percent—and emergency care utilization by nearly comparable amounts—and have reduced total cost by as much as $12,900 per engaged Medicare beneficiary.[61] All this is concurrent with a high level of beneficiary and family satisfaction for services that are desperately needed and too often not provided.

This denotes more than incremental improvement. Impact of this magnitude is not typical of a care management program. Yet, the reported and published results speak for themselves. They also create an imperative that these types of services become the standard of care, and the expectation of any patient and family facing advanced illness.

The Advanced Care Project

To help make that happen, C-TAC and the AHIP Foundation's Institute for Health Systems Solutions (IHSS) have joined forces on The Advanced Care Project. This project brings together innovators from health systems and health plans, along with advocacy groups, faith-based organizations and others, to develop a clinical model of care for those with advanced illness, as well as a payment model that supports the transition from fee-for-service toward performance- and risk-based reimbursement. According to Carmela Bocchino, Executive Vice President at America's Health Insurance Plans (AHIP), the Advanced Care Project "will make 'the right way the easy way' for hospitals, health systems, physician groups, other clinicians and health plans—as well as for nursing homes, hospices, and community-based organizations—to provide high quality care for patients and families living with advanced illness."[62]

Building on the progress that has been made, *The Advanced Care Project* recognizes that the barriers to improving advanced illness care do not stem from a lack of new ideas. Innovative models (such as those mentioned above) are already producing scalable, replicable and sustainable solutions, and some have already received support from the Center for Medicare and Medicaid Innovation. The challenge, instead, is to spread and test these new models in a coordinated way to develop national models of clinical care and payment that will be widely adopted by providers and payers, including Medicare.

Based on the principles outlined earlier in this chapter (see page 3), the advanced care model provides a new transitional pathway from cure to comfort. Advanced care occupies a specific position in the continuum of clinical services available to patients with progressive chronic illness:

Figure 1. Complex care management provides intensive medical management to patients who are expected to recover. Advanced care provides comprehensive care management to people who have poor prospects for full recovery. Hospice provides care management for patients who are terminal. Palliative care provides symptom management and support at any stage of illness.

Advanced care is not a new service line. It is a re-engineering of care delivery that integrates and actively links settings of care delivery that are now disconnected—hospitals, primary care offices and clinics, specialists, home and community. It also re-engineers care delivery by leveraging the capabilities of current service components like inpatient and office-based case management, palliative care, home health and hospice. Through repurposing and retraining, new care teams can increase clinical effectiveness, promote patient choice and reduce operational costs by avoiding unwanted hospital admissions and eliminating unnecessary services, tests and procedures.

Advanced care is the "missing link" between current recovery-oriented care models and comfort care. Complex care management, sometimes called "hot spotting," serves patients with chronic illness who undergo frequent emergency visits and hospitalizations because their condition/s are not well managed. Candidates for complex care management are not facing imminent death. The goals of complex care management are recovery from acute episodes and reduction of unnecessary utilization. Patients receive more focused and intensive medical management than they would through normal doctor visits.

Palliative care, on the other hand, provides an extra layer of service to patients who suffer from the time they are diagnosed until they die. Palliative care prevents and relieves suffering through early identification, assessment and treatment of pain and other problems whether they are physical, psychosocial or spiritual. As a medical subspecialty, palliative care is provided episodically, generally through physicians or advanced-practice nurses. Hospice provides comprehensive comfort care for individuals with a life expectancy of six months or less. To enroll, they must forego any Medicare-reimbursed treatment aimed at prolonging life.

Individuals with advanced illness have multiple complications and their ability to function is usually reduced. In general, they have endured multiple hospitalizations, each one longer and more complicated than the last, and they have emerged from the hospital in worse shape than when they were admitted. They may have benefited from complex care management in the past, but these strategies are no longer applicable. Likewise, palliative care clinicians may have seen these patients in the hospital, clinic or occasionally at home, but the more comprehensive management measures employed by advanced care can provide them additional benefits.

The Advanced Care model integrates care across multiple dimensions. A "team of teams" approach coordinates care across clinical settings and over time. Specially trained, physician-directed interdisciplinary teams are placed in hospitals, physician practices, homes and the community. These teams connect with patients, families and each other in real time through electronic health records (EHR) and sophisticated telephone management. The Advanced Care model incorporates specific, proven strategies that include:

- Targeting the high-risk, high-cost advanced illness population (3-4% of Medicare beneficiaries)
- Providing comprehensive transitional and post-acute care
- Establishing reliable and efficient handoff processes among teams and settings
- Furnishing interdisciplinary high-impact visits in hospital, office/clinic and home
- Employing proactive tele-management
- Promoting real-time communication across all clinical settings
- Engaging the personal physician (primary care and/or specialist) as a core member of the team
- Delivering advance care planning over time at the person's own pace and in the preferred setting
- Educating, counsel and support individuals, families and caregivers in self-management
- Extending the reach of palliative care into the community
- Optimizing electronic medical record or care management systems

Advanced care fills the gaps between intensive medical management of complex chronic illness, palliative care and hospice, and it also promotes appropriate use of these services. It assures that intensive management can continue if needed but that comfort measures are also provided. Advanced care ensures good clinical outcomes, maximizes personal choice, prevents unwanted procedures and hospitalization and makes the care of serious illness more affordable.

Health Plans: New Approaches to Payment

The road to large-scale implementation runs through health plans and their ability to influence how health care is provided. In providing advanced illness care management, health plans have a role, an opportunity and an obligation to insist such services and programs become available to members. That means they also have to provide the necessary resources and payments for implementation, measure their results and impact, and assure that providers are appropriately compensated for these services. They also must develop and implement appropriate provider incentives and requirements to assure that guidance and support is available to members/patients.

The Advanced Care Project has developed the following key principles that should serve as the foundation for the development of advanced care payment models.

1. The payment model should encourage high-quality, person-driven, coordinated care by:
    *   Ensuring that incentives to coordinate care, improve quality, and respect personal wishes regarding care are aligned across the full range of settings and providers.
    *   Promoting operational integration and care coordination across acute, post-acute and long-term care settings. This will be most easily achieved in the more flexible environment of population-based approaches to care and coverage.

2. The payment model should augment broader health system transformation efforts by:
    *   Reinforcing new models supported by evidence that they are effective and undergoing adoption. This is likely to lower transaction costs, confusion, and complexity by leveraging emerging knowledge and infrastructure.
    *   Providing a bridge to population- and risk-based models. The movement away from fee-for-service toward new reimbursement that provides incentives for high-value care will take time to accomplish. The payment model for advanced care must account for current providers' needs to maintain margins in order to invest in new care management services, while providing flexibility over time so that payments can evolve to support shared risk and

population management.
- Supporting different coverage systems, including traditional Medicare, Medicare Advantage, Medicaid and commercial coverage.
- Aligning discussion and collaboration among health plans, other payers, and providers. Initiatives to adopt common standards for quality or other measures could lower transaction costs and promote adoption of new clinical models. The payment model should also be capable of independent implementation.

3. A successful payment model should accomplish the following goals:
   - Support broad-based provider investment in advanced care capability
   - Create opportunities for return on this investment
   - Contribute to broad-based movement from fee-for-service
   - Build on broad-based developments in care and payment models

4. This model could use a blended approach using the following components:
   - Existing fee-for-service payment arrangements (to support broad provider participation)
   - Pre-paid, non-visit based care management fees tied to specific care delivery capabilities for targeted individuals with advanced illness (to ensure sufficient investment in the capacity and tools necessary to deliver best practice AIM)
   - Value-based or population-based components that integrate attainment of quality and outcomes goals

The Patient-Centered Medical Home (PCMH) potentially provides a preliminary framework for a payment model that applies these principles. This is not to suggest that the Advanced Care Project care model should be incorporated into the PCMH. Rather, it acknowledges that PCMH provides a blended payment structure (commonly FFS based payments, with a payment for care coordination, quality-based payments, and shared savings or shared risk component) that is designed to encourage higher quality, coordinated care and that is becoming increasingly familiar among payers and providers.

While the development of a standard payment model for advanced care is ideal, the advanced care model currently can be supported by implementing multiple payment options through risk-bearing structures such as managed care or ACOs and by refining current payment innovations (such as bundled payment and population-specific ACOs) through payer-provider partnerships.

To support further payment development, *The Advanced Care Project* will convene a payer/provider workgroup to develop consensus on principles such as those outlined above, and design a pro forma payment model. The financial model would depict the relationship of variables and standard assumptions across care settings as they relate to (e.g.) expenses, benefits, and revenues, in order to help create a generally accepted, standardized but flexible analytic framework to aid in payment design.[63] The model would seek to align incentives and provide a bridge from existing payment systems to one that is increasing based on value, risk-based and performance-based payments, and consistent with broader payment reform efforts.

The examples cited in this chapter demonstrate that expanding the availability and use of best practice delivery models for people needing advanced care is in the clinical and business interest of health plans, as well as their patients and their families. But, if we hope to realize the potential demonstrated by these models, providers, health plans and government will have to cooperate and work together on large-scale implementation. This will require a strong national, coordinated effort to engage and educate both the public and professionals and to advocate for public policy changes in the states and in Washington. Chapter 6 addresses the role of advocacy and public policy in detail.

CHAPTER 6

The Role of Policy and Advocacy
Charlie Sabatino and Mark Schoeberl

"I was the son of a mother and father who suffered from two distinct and very terrible diseases – one of them cancer and the other one Alzheimer's... I saw first-hand the importance of thinking of sound mind and body about what you would want done, how you would want your life to be extended, and how you would want to be treated. Being a caregiver, my wife and I and my brother and sister and their spouses tried desperately to take care of my mom in the later stages of Alzheimer's, which is a very challenging disease and a very challenging responsibility. And once again, having not discussed the "what-ifs" when my mom was of sound mind and body, we were guessing in trying to figure out the right thing to do... Everybody has to make up their own mind. But not having the discussion, not knowing the facts...is what we're trying to avoid."[64]

—Senator Johnny Isakson (R-GA)

"...not unlike most everybody in this room I come to this not only from a policy making standpoint and many of you from a medical standpoint but everyone one of us has some kind of personal standpoint. I think about the fact that my mom had Alzheimer's for more than a decade and she had parents who all had the same affiliation with the disease. She didn't even speak her last eight or nine years...yet even with all that kind of family history pre-warning... and you would have thought being a relatively informed citizen that we would have sat down within our own family and had the kind of conversations when my mom could still weigh in with our pastor and others..."[65]

—Senator Mark Warner (D-VA)

Senator Isakson's and Senator Warner's stories, and the stories of countless others willing to share similar experiences, remind us that we are all equally affected by the very human and delicate issues associated with advanced illness and end of life care. Whether we are U.S. Senators, skilled workers, accomplished professionals, or trained health care providers, we are the spouses, sons and daughters, siblings, caregivers, and friends of loved ones facing advanced illness.

These stories also challenge us to consider what, if anything, could have been done to improve these experiences. What were some of the missed opportunities, obstacles or barriers that inhibited the Senators' mothers from sharing their care wishes with their families when they were of "sound mind and body"? Most importantly, what can and should we be doing better for all families that may one day face similar decisions?

We cannot view these stories as simply "successes" or "failures," but rather as teaching moments. They occur numerous times a day in communities all across this country—raising new questions, reinforcing concerns, and in some cases, demonstrating effective solutions. In this chapter, we are focusing on how more effective public policy can improve the care that patients facing advanced illness receive. Or more specifically, how and where thoughtful public policy can be a positive influence and catalyst to assist us on the path forward to transforming care for this population.

But first, what do we mean by "public policy"? For our purposes in this chapter, we define public policy as "the sum of government activities, whether pursued directly or through agents, as those activities have an influence on the lives of citizens."[66] In health care, public policy—including policies governing payment for health care services—is a very powerful force, for better or for worse, in shaping care delivery. Such policy can be influenced at a number of levels and by various means, including federal, state and municipal legislation, regulations and the policies and procedures of public and private institutions, payers and providers.

There are significantly divergent opinions on the proper role of government, whether at the federal, state or community level, in the delivery of health care, but the influence that current public policy can exert on delivery models is undeniable. Regardless of whether care is provided directly through government programs such as traditional Medicare and Medicaid, public/private models, or commercial market, public policy impacts the rules and basic set of services patients with advanced illness and their families might expect to receive.

Finally, it is important to note that public policy is a reflection of societies' will, values and priorities. As we consider the factors that have influenced the public policy that is impacting advanced care today in this country, and what it will take to change things moving forward, it is essential to recognize that change cannot occur in a vacuum. First and foremost, it requires all of us with stories similar to Senators Isakson's and Warner's, to ask why we have to accept a status quo that does not actively offer, solicit, respect, and adhere to the care and treatment wishes of patients facing advanced illness. We must also continue to explore, implement and evaluate innovative new care models and identify public policies that can facilitate their broader implementation. And, we must work together with Congress and our elected officials to keep our focus on what is necessary to meet the needs of patient and their families.

So, what is "good" policy and how do we develop public policy that actually translates into enhanced experiences for individuals and families at the ground level? For instance, can we create systems that provide the kinds of care choices patients actually want? How can we ensure that individuals fully engage in thorough, in-depth discussions with their care team regarding their wishes rather than simply "checking a box" to fulfill a requirement? As fundamental as these questions may sound, these are some of the key dilemmas we struggle with and must confront when considering public policy and its potential for positive influence (meaningful discussions) and unintended consequences (check-boxes).

Given that advanced illness care is such a medically, socially and personally complex issue, we face inherent challenges in developing consensus on what constitutes effective public policy in this arena. This issue, perhaps like no other, touches on a wide range of interests involving a diverse set of stakeholders that includes individuals, payers, providers and others. It also holds the added challenge of dealing with issues in which individuals hold very intense personal emotions, beliefs, and experiences.

So let us begin with a brief history of the issues surrounding advanced illness and how public policy changed over time.

The Political Process and Current Landscape

For years, policymakers have struggled with how to improve care for people needing advanced care. The establishment of Medicare and Medicaid in 1965 set the stage for a less personal, institutionally-based model of care by making Medicaid nursing home coverage mandatory for states and by providing relatively brief periods of post-hospital care for patients in nursing homes or from home health agencies. Then, in 1982, the introduction of the Medicare Hospice Benefit kicked off a period of historic improvements in the delivery of advanced illness care.

Hospice establishes a template for advanced illness care using key principles such as highly-coordinated care across settings, close collaboration with local community groups, palliative care, and continuous discussions regarding an individual's treatment choices and preferences that support and enhance person-centered and family-centered care delivery. The concept behind hospice care began to gather movement in the 1960's and gained credibility through Congressional hearings and demonstration projects in the 1970's. A formal benefit was later made permanent by Congress in 1986 and soon became a well-recognized, key component of the care continuum in the mid 1990's.[67] Throughout its development, the concept of hospice has gained support from key leaders on both sides of the aisle.

In addition to the development of hospice, legislative bills such as the *Patient Self-Determination Act of 1990*[68] and the *Medicare Prescription Drug, Improvement, and Modernization Act of 2003*[69] have paved the way in advanced illness policy and have led to the development of promising approaches for providing and reimbursing services and treatments for advanced illness care.

In recent years, however, as the debate over health care reform intensified in 2009, the issue of advanced illness care has become increasingly politicized. The Centers for Medicare and Medicaid Services (CMS) in 2010 proposed a Medicare regulation to authorize voluntary advance care planning consultations between individuals (or their surrogates) and physicians as part of the Medicare annual wellness exam. However, this was later rescinded within days as a result of political pressures. A similar provision was also included in the *Patient Protection and Affordable Care Act* (PPACA) but was later eliminated due to political arguments regarding the purpose and intent of the provision.[70]

That something relatively reasonable and seemingly straightforward—reimbursing doctors for these consultations—could cause such a political eruption is indicative of the challenges we face. Without casting aspersions on either side of a legitimate debate on the issue of reimbursing doctors for these consultations, it became increasingly clear that those opposed to PPACA were citing this provision as an example of government's overreach into health care. They suggested that "death panels" would decide who would live and die and that, with an increased focus on cost issues, doctors would become biased towards pursuing the lowest-cost option with their patients and potentially remove care at the end of life. Notwithstanding that most reasonable interpretations of the statue concluded that such descriptions were inherently wrong, the vitriolic public policy and media debate that ensued distracted from the core principle that government and other payers should encourage and facilitate doctor-patient communication, not suppress it. The provision was subsequently dropped from the legislation.

The political controversy regarding the language and messaging of the government's role in end-of-life care likely deterred some legislators from actively participating in the issue given the political risks and gains. The key is that we must frame the issue around people, families, and caregivers, focusing policy discussions squarely on one key principle— **care must be compassionate, person-centered, and directed to meet the goals, wishes, and preferences of individuals and their families.**

With the experience of PPACA behind us, a few active Congressional champions have risen to the cause, creating legislative bills that have sought to expand coverage for advance care planning, develop advanced illness demonstration models, and establish comprehensive supports for families and caregivers. Some of these are incremental bills and others are more comprehensive:

- *Care Planning Act of 2013* (introduced by Sens. Warner (D-VA) and Isakson (R-GA))
  A more evolved version of the Senior Navigation and Planning Act of 2012, this bill provides coverage for both advance care planning services as well as coordination services to those with advanced illness by a hospice or other provider through an interdisciplinary team.

- *Medicare Choices Empowerment and Protection Act* (introduced by Sens. Tom Coburn (R-OK) and Chris Coons (D-DE) in April 2014) *This bill would have provided a small, one-time fee for beneficiaries who voluntarily certify to CMS that they have created an advance directive.*

- *Personalize Your Care Act of 2013* (introduced by Reps. Blumenauer (D-OR) and Phil Roe (R-TN)) *This bill establishes a requirement to provide Medicare & Medicaid coverage for advance care planning consultations every five years or whenever there is a change in an individual's health status.*

- *Palliative Care and Hospice Education and Training Act of 2013* (introduced by Sen. Wyden (D-OR) and Reps. Eliot Engel (D-NY) and Tom Reed (R-NY) in the House) *This bill would have awarded grants or contracts to establish palliative care and hospice education centers, schools, teaching hospitals, and support for Graduate Medical Education (GME) programs to teach palliative care medicine and distribute academic career awards to advanced illness practitioners.*

- *Americans Giving Care to Elders Act of 2013* (introduced by Sen. Klobuchar (D-MN) and Sen. Mikulski (D-MD)) *The bill would allow families caring for certain aging family members to qualify for federal tax credits.*

- *Advance Planning and Compassionate Care Act of 2009* (introduced by Sen. Jay Rockefeller (D-WV) and Sen. Susan Collins (R-ME)) *This act would have authorized coverage for advance care planning under Medicare, Medicaid, and CHIP, launched an online advance care planning toolkit, and created grants for states to develop advance directive registries.*

- *Life Sustaining Treatment Preferences Act of 2009* (introduced by Earl Blumenauer (D-OR))
  This act would have authorized Medicare coverage for consultations regarding orders for life sustaining treatment, and established state grants for POLST programs.

- *Preserving Access to Hospice Act of 2008* (introduced by Sen. Jim Inhofe (R-OK) and Rep. John Sullivan (R-OK) in the House)
  This bill directs MedPAC to (1) study hospice as a substitute for other acute care alternatives, (2) identify optimal stays in hospice, and (3) determine reasons behind consistently low average length of stays.

In 2013, C-TAC released a report – the *Advanced Illness Policy Review: The Landscape for Improving Advanced Illness Care in America* (also known as the "Policy Compendium," available at thectac.org, to assess the success and comprehensiveness of current legislation in this arena. The Compendium reviewed legislation from the 109th Congress through the current 113th Congressional session—from approximately 2005 to the present.[71] From this review, it is clear that the primary strategy for change has been to seek incremental reform of selective barriers. In addition, it is important to note that, within the past 3-4 years, there has been a notable surge in legislative bills that have been introduced in the Congress. Nevertheless, real policy change to improve advanced care has yet to be accomplished.

Strong committee leadership from both parties and houses are essential to moving the debate along. In 2013, Ways and Means Committee Chairman, Dave Camp (R-MI); Ranking Member, Sandy Levin (D-MI); and Senate Finance Committee Chairman, Max Baucus (D-MT), and Ranking Member, Orrin Hatch (R-UT), launched a bipartisan, bicameral effort to enhance Medicare Post-Acute Reform by asking stakeholders to submit comments on policy and legislation recommendations regarding quality measurement, discharge planning, and payment models for this population. Sen. Ron Wyden (D-OR) continued support of the bill when he succeeded Sen. Baucus as Finance Committee Chairman in 2014. They later released a discussion draft for the Improving Medicare Post-Acute Care Transformation Act (IMPACT) in 2014 (H.R. 4994 and S. 2553) to gather stakeholder opinions on these issues.[72] The resounding theme from the more than 70 letters received was the need for standardized post-acute assessment data across Medicare post-acute care provider settings. The *IMPACT Act of 2014* is a worthwhile attempt to move forward on the longstanding policy goal of collecting relevant, standardized data to inform future payment reforms. The final version of the bill was signed into law in October 2014 after passing both the House and Senate. This is the kind of approach needed to enhance efficiency and higher quality while still protecting patients' access to appropriate services in post-acute care.

While this represents an encouraging step forward, we still need to develop legislation that includes specific provisions to address the advanced illness population—one with high care needs.

Building bipartisan, bicameral efforts such as the collaboration for the *IMPACT Act* helps to offer traction, attention, and credibility to these issues. Cultivating these strategic relationships and partnerships across party lines means that, once reform legislation is drafted, it will be well recognized and will have a higher likelihood of passing. Ensuring that our system provides care that adheres to our loved one's last wishes and preferences—regardless of what those wishes encompass—is something for which we all aim.

Moving Forward

Given this history and the more recent positive examples such as the *IMPACT Act*, how can we best work together to help ensure that promising public policy opportunities continue to advance and effective legislation and regulatory change are achieved?

The first step is education, which must precede policy development. Policymakers must truly understand the systematic gaps and deficiencies in our care delivery before looking into sweeping reforms. They must understand the impact that policy has on people—everyone from health care administrators and providers, all the way to the most important group affected—those who must actually face advanced illness; patients and their loved ones. One reason policy development has failed in the past is because it has been developed without a strong evidence base of strategies and models that have proven to be successful.

Building Policy

Many leaders and policymakers across the spectrum seek to gain a better grasp of the high-level issues, themes, and barriers related to advanced care, but are unsure of where and even how to begin. What are the current barriers in the system? In order to understand these systematic gaps in care delivery, policymakers need the proper resources. They need to hear from objective experts in the field. They also need trusted, substantive resources to help them better understand these issues. Documents such as C-TAC's Policy Framework[73] and Policy Agenda[74] are examples of useful toolkits that policymakers can use to hear directly from experts in the field.

At its core, policy development is a process. Policy is always changing and evolving. It is an ongoing process that must be continuously revised and reviewed to ensure that it is successfully impacting patients and families. The most effective starting point to learn what works—and what doesn't—is to listen to the voices of those who are directly immersed in the issue, whether they are the leaders within their respective health systems, providers, or the patients and families themselves.

So, how do we listen? How do we gain this kind of insight? Building upon Senator Isakson's story at the opening of this chapter, the following stories go beyond simply raising awareness of the issue. These narratives serve as insights into the types of system-wide problems and issues that hinder care delivery. They highlight the kinds of work that must be achieved level in order to achieve comprehensive reform.

The Policy "Roadmap to Reform"

"As my 88-year-old father-in-law was in decline with eight different chronic conditions, he had more specialists than we could keep track of, and nobody was steering the ship. Most of all, his pain was poorly managed, but finding an outpatient palliative care physician was impossible, even in a city like Los Angeles. He resisted hospice mainly because he thought that meant he was giving up, so he continued to suffer and experience recurring runs to the emergency room. When he finally agreed to home hospice, his care and condition improved dramatically, and during the final month he lived under hospice he was comfortable, he had heartfelt conversations with all 11 of his children, and he died in peace and dignity in his home. It was a good death, but the period of serious, progressive illness before hospice was a nightmare, because hospice-type care is kept out of reach until the last moments of life."

—IOM, Dying in America: Improving Quality and Honoring Individual Preferences Near the End of Life, p. 2-5

Why was the period of serious, progressive illness before hospice a nightmare? With eight different chronic conditions and a specialist for each condition, no one was looking at the whole person and talking about the father-in-law's goals of care, his overall prognosis and care options, and asking him what would make this stage of his life better. These conversations need to take place with him and his family and a care team well before the decision to use hospice. These conversations are at the core of advance care planning.

Successful models across the country such as those described in Chapter 5 have used broad approaches to advance care planning and care delivery and have emphasized the importance in developing compassionate, trusting relationships between patients and physicians and care choices that are meaningful to seriously ill individuals. This allows individuals to be engaged in a comprehensive decision-making process through a collaborative partnership with family, clinicians, and care teams in order to clearly establish goals of care and implement them.[75] When should these conversations begin? The Institute of Medicine's recent report, *Dying in America: Improving Quality and Honoring Individual Preferences Near the End of Life*, recommends a *life-cycle model* of advance care planning that begins at adulthood and continues throughout life, changing as one's health circumstances and diagnoses change. In the father-in-law's case, these conversations should have happened regularly, years in advance of his eventually terminal illness and throughout his illness; and if he were to become unable to speak for himself, a health care agent named in his advance directive should be continuing the conversation for him.

Goals of care change with time, condition and life events. Good public policy can help normalize these discussions throughout the life course, so that one's lifetime values and choices may be fully known, respected and acted upon across the care continuum. During a roundtable hosted in May 2014 by the Senate Special Committee on Aging, *Continuing the Conversation: The Role of Health Care Providers in Advance Care Planning*, Senator Sheldon Whitehouse (D-RI) remarked: "...there is inevitable grief around a death, but what we can do is lift the shadow off of that grief of guilt, frustration, resentment, anger, and all of the other emotions that are brought up when people aren't allowed to die in a way that is comfortable to them and consistent with their beliefs and with their wishes and that's a much easier thing to process."

Policy Goal # 1

Normalize advance care planning through counseling, and meaningful discussion of prognosis, goals of care, personal values and treatment preferences.

Some legislative bills have included provisions for patient-physician consultations to be renewed every five years so that individuals have the chance to actively review and renew their positions.[76] Other bills, beyond providing reimbursements to incentivize and promote these continued patient-physician discussions, have supported grants and incentives for the creation of public campaigns, 24/7 hotlines, websites, brochures, and a multitude of informational resources in order to spread awareness of advance care planning and promote patient engagement and empowerment on a much broader scale.[77] In the current political climate, these bills were seen by many as unrealistic, costly additions to the menu of government benefits. They also failed to fully address greater systems' parameters of advanced care delivery.

Even if patients are able to engage with their physicians, sustain these necessary conversations, and document their wishes, how do we ensure proper portability across state borders? Here, a major burden weighs heavily with the states on easing well-intended—but sometimes onerous—requirements that patients follow detailed legal formalities in creating documents to express their health care wishes. Examples include requiring specific, prescribed phrases for authorizing certain wishes, required disclosures or warnings, standardized statutory forms, extensive limitations on who may serve as an agent or proxy, or restrictions on who may serve as a witness.[78] These legal restrictions prevent directives from being valid across state borders, and sometimes, even within state borders. Thus, it is presently impossible to offer the public an advance directive that is considered legally valid under the laws of all states.[79]

Congress has consciously refrained from proposing a federal advance directive because health care decision-making procedures are traditionally rooted in state law. However, access to completed advance directives is a different matter, and some policymakers have suggested creating or supporting a standard, uniform repository at the federal level where providers and patients across care settings and types can access advance care planning documents. This option, if pursued, should be thoughtfully integrated into the expansion of health information technology used by health care providers.

Health information technologies (HIT) hold great promise in providing that individual's goals of care and wishes are known. They also play a key role in ensuring quality, efficient delivery systems of the future for individuals needing advanced illness care. If successful, they will improve communication among individuals and providers as well as emergency, inpatient, home and community-based services and will ensure more efficient integration among silos of services. HIT efforts must also include the development of standards, protocols and incentives to ensure quality and efficacy across settings and providers, and the protection of individually identifiable health information.

Policy Goal # 2

Build health information technologies that promote advance care planning documentation and effective information sharing across time, place and provider with appropriate safeguards for privacy.

Expanding access, incentivizing these services, and reducing administrative burdens requires a collaborative, multistep approach across federal, state, and regional levels. Advance care planning is clearly a necessary step in the process and requires a continuous process involving patients, families, providers, and the entire care team.

As individuals engage in these discussions with their physicians or face advanced illness, how are they cared for and supported by their friends and family? Our next topic will address the immense support that caregivers provide for their loved ones and the duties they must fulfill.

Caregiver Challenges

"Ten years ago my mother-in-law was widowed and moved from her home in Monroeville to a house on my street... For the past five years as her physical health deteriorated rapidly and her mind succumbed to advancing Alzheimer's disease, my wife and I became her caregivers. All household chores, both inside and out, had to be done by us. We provided all her meals, did all her shopping, scheduled and drove her to all her appointments, administered all her medicines multiple times a day, took care of her finances and saw to all her other day-to-day

needs. At the same time, we were still fulfilling all those same responsibilities for our children plus the added commitment of their individual school, social and leisure activities... The physical demands of taking care of two families is tiring. Two yards to cut, drives to shovel, houses to clean, extra meals, extra laundry, extra appointments. The extras are never-ending. The emotional demands and time constraints are harder. If a child has a therapy appointment and Gran has a doctor's appointment, which is more important? Unfortunately, there aren't enough reliable, affordable services for the elderly. What services are out there are not widely known and often only discovered when commiserating with someone else in the same situation..."

—Tom Moore, witness testimony at "The Sandwich Generation Squeeze: Confronting the Middle Class Struggle to Raise Kids, Care for Aging Parents, and Scrape Together Enough for Retirement in Today's Economy"[80]

This hearing, held by the Senate Committee on Aging, offered a unique opportunity for families to tell their story as members of a generation that must care for both their elders and children. As a member of the "Sandwich" Generation, Mr. Moore and his wife felt pressured to "choose" between attending the needs of an aging parent and assisting their children in their activities.

It also revealed that many caregivers feel lost in a complex maze of financial duties and emotional burdens. Before we jump to develop policy that will provide more needed supports and services, we must ask whether we truly understand caregiver needs in the first place. While we know more supportive services are needed, we need to build a stronger evidence base identifying the range and intensity of services needed to accommodate our society's diversity of chronic conditions, cultures, and health literacy levels. A few policy bills have suggested directing federal agencies to conduct in-depth assessments of the kinds of needs caregivers have. [81]

Policy Goal # 3
Ensure a full range of supports and services to caregivers and families facing advanced illness.

To offer more educational resources to caregivers, some bills have authorized additional funding for a national family caregiver support program to direct family caregivers to the proper resources and assistance or creating a national resource center on family caregiving.[82] Finally, other legislative bills have focused on offering tax deductions for caregivers, expanding counseling and mental health services, and increasing access to respite services. While caregivers have received increased attention in public discourse, they still are largely taken for granted as a given part of the patient's environment, rather than being viewed as an integral part of the care team deserving of professional support and material assistance.

Advance care planning, educational materials, and supports and services for caregivers can be enhanced by effective policy. But the payment and delivery system structures currently in use primarily address only treatment procedures and fail to deal with advanced care as an integrated constellation of supports and services geared to achieve the patient's goals for living with advanced illness. From a broader perspective, system-wide coverage, payment and delivery system reform plays a profoundly important role.

This issue is a tremendously complex one. Many efforts have been made in both the public and private sector to advance delivery systems, implement payment reform, and enhance quality measure development to better assess the success of these new models. A few of the narratives below will touch upon some of the key issues in advanced care delivery.

Paying for Quality, Not Just Quantity

"It was a year later when my father was diagnosed with Stage IV cancer.

And he asked for just one thing. He wanted to die at home. And it plunged my brothers and me into a world of advance directives and the world of adequate palliative care that no family should have to try to navigate on its own. Now, I say every day how grateful I am for hospice. We could never have met his wishes without the help of hospice. But every day was a fight around palliative care, a concern about whether we had "checked every box" we needed to check to get him some care but not have him end up at the hospital where he didn't want to be..."
—Senator Elizabeth Warren (D-MA)

Here is an example where the system got it right. How? In her narrative, Senator Warren expresses her gratitude for the care and compassion that hospice care provided to her and her family in her father's last days. At its core, the principles of hospice incorporate the kinds of strategies that are needed for persons with significant physical, emotional, and spiritual needs—including highly coordinated care across settings, utilizing interdisciplinary teams of clinicians, social workers, and spiritual advisors, close collaboration with local community groups, and continuous discussion regarding the individuals' personal and health care goals. These principles can serve as a template to develop a framework to reform care delivery for the broader population with advanced illness.

Having access to this service allowed Senator Warren and her family to follow their fathers' last wishes. However, despite the availability of these great benefits and services, many of the administrative requirements—including those for receiving hospice or palliative care interventions in home or community-based settings—prevent individuals from accessing the care they need. For hospice, these barriers include the six months to live prognosis (requiring providers to declare that individuals have six months or less to live in order to be eligible for hospice care) and the requirement to forgo curative care. While considerable research demonstrates the extensive benefits of electing hospice care, including in many cases actually lengthening life by improving the quality of life for both patients and families, the context in which many patients have to consider hospice too frequently leads to false impressions.[83]

As we deal with regulatory and administrative barriers, issues with care coordination, lack of standards of care, integration of social support services, and reimbursement issues for advance care, we must carefully pinpoint the gaps and deficiencies in the system, test innovative models and approaches to improving care, and then develop legislation that can remove the barriers and improve care.

On the regulatory level, many new approaches are being developed by the Centers for Medicare and Medicaid Services through projects such as the Hospice Medicare Care Choices Model,[84] the Comprehensive End Stage Renal Disease (ESRD) Care Initiative,[85] the Dual Eligible Demonstration Project [86], the Medicare Coordinated Care Demo[87], the Independence at Home Demonstration Project[88], Medicare Acute Care Demonstration Project[89], and others that allow providers the financial flexibility to explore innovative strategies and approaches to enhance care delivery for this population and experiment with new payment and coverage models. Delivery reform in itself is a very difficult topic and policy must be carefully crafted to incorporate those evidence-based best practices that have shown to produce successful results.

Policy Goal # 4
Ensure person-centered care management that effectively bridges acute, post-acute, and long-term care settings, treatment and time.

Stories like those of Senators Warren, Isakson and Warner expose different faults in the system through personal narratives. Each person's perspective helps to examine the barriers in the system on a micro level. However, through a broader perspective, how do we obtain a better understanding of the struggles that patients face as they move through fragmented systems? How do we objectively measure the needs of patients and gauge their experience? Developing quality measures is crucial to answering these questions.

With an issue as complex as payment and delivery reform, developing proper metrics and standardizing these measures across care settings is essential, primarily for three reasons: (1) to educate policymakers and stakeholders on the current gaps and needs in the system, (2) to drive payment and delivery reform that will pay for quality and not merely quantity of care, and (3) to assure accountability. The data collected from quality measurement systems help us to approach the issue on a macro-level by developing more whole-scale, larger views of the system. Quality measures must be enhanced to encompass even those aspects of the care delivery that are difficult to measure, such as the level of shared decision-making and the quality of patient-physician discussions.

Policy Goal # 5

Support expanded research as a key tool to improve care delivery practices and strengthen quality standards for individuals and families facing advanced illness.

The Affordable Care Act created a public-private partnership through the National Quality Forum (NQF), the U. S. Department of Health and Human Services (HHS) and the Hospice Quality Reporting Program. This partnership implemented the Performance Measurement Coordination Strategy for Hospice and Palliative Care, which focuses on developing strategies and approaches to promote common goals across hospice and palliative care programs that can be readily implemented.[90]

Training and Professional Engagement

Lastly, a key component of proper care delivery involves the careful training and engagement of a team of interdisciplinary professionals.

"In 2004, Aetna decided to launch the Compassionate Care SM Program

to allow members access to the care they wanted to help manage their illness. It also covers supportive services not normally covered under Medicare or private insurance. Research demonstrates that there is a significant gap between the care people would like to receive at the end of life and the care they actually receive. Our intent is to provide specialized case management to meet the unique needs of members with advanced illness. We have also had strong results in the Medicare population, primarily due to the strong case management that is part of Compassionate Care. The benefits of the program are clear to our members and their families. One of our case managers shared the following note after a discussion with the wife of a member: "Wife stated member passed away with hospice. Much emotional support given to spouse. She talked about what a wonderful life they had together, their children, all of the people's lives that he touched… she said she is so grateful for the outpouring of love. Also stated that hospice was wonderful, as well as everyone at the doctor's office, and everyone here at Aetna."

—Randall S. Krakauer, MD, Chief Medical Officer,

Medicare, Aetna

This story is clear. This and other models work. Individuals facing advanced illness must navigate a complex delivery system in a time when they are vulnerable. Advanced illness treatment requires a comprehensive, team-based approach to deliver high quality care and investing in the time and resources to enhance the professional care team is key.

When the care team is carefully trained to treat the person rather than the patient, the individual has a more fulfilling experience, as noted by Dr. Krakauer above. If physicians and other health care professionals are to engage effectively in person-centered care and advance care planning, they need the skills to communicate with and engage patients and family in that process. Until recently, this kind of training has been largely absent, especially from physician education. It must become a basic component of education for all physicians and other professionals with direct patient contact.

An important new role that has evolved as part of care teams is that of care manager or navigator. Care managers or navigators can be especially trained in dealing with individuals with advanced illness or chronic conditions and serve as the main point of contact for all the person's questions, concerns, and care needs as he or she goes through the process. Navigators or care managers do not take over the doctor's role; rather they supplement it and ensure that the patient's and family's communication with the doctor is optimal.

Policy Goal # 6
Build a health care workforce educated and equipped with the clinical and social skills to enable people with advanced illness and their families and caregivers to navigate their treatment, care, and support options according to their values and preferences.

On the policy front, providing incentives for a wide range of initiatives for both allopathic and osteopathic care teams to increase professional engagement in the palliative care arena or providing grants for continuing education could be useful first steps in the process. Legislation such as the Palliative Care & Hospice Education and Training Act (PCHETA), introduced by Sen. Ron Wyden (D-OR), Rep. Eliot Engel (D-NY) and Rep. Tom Reed (R-NY), contains provisions to establish palliative care and hospice education centers, support continuing education and retraining opportunities, disseminate information related to palliative care among the provider community, establish academic career awards, and authorize grants to medical schools and teaching hospitals to teach palliative medicine.

Advocating and Implementing Comprehensive Reform

Although it may be difficult to identify one specific proposal—whether regulatory or legislative—that can singlehandedly transform advanced care, policy makers must work closely with stakeholders to achieve comprehensive reform. The C-TAC Policy Agenda, the September 2014 Institute of Medicine (IOM) report, *Dying in America: Improving Quality and Honoring Individual Preferences Near the End of Life*, and other recent books and publications highlight key areas where experts agree that further reform is needed. At the core is a consensus that policy objectives should focus on ensuring that individuals receive high-quality, person-centered care delivered in a way that honors their wishes, choices and preferences. The publication and dissemination of these reports will help spark a thoughtful and meaningful dialogue among stakeholders, elevate the status and priority of these issues, and ultimately draw the proper attention and support from decision-makers in Congress and the Administration.

Grassroots campaigns, national communications programs and polling data can be used to effectively engage public audiences to advocate for these issues. In addition, promoting cross-sector collaboration across a wide range of payers, providers, insurers and community-based organizations will help grow and develop the evidence base for innovative and effective strategies the enhance advanced care delivery.

In addition to C-TAC, other coalitions have been instrumental in advocating for advanced illness care and end-of-life issues. They have been diligent in their advocacy efforts to encourage policymakers to increase access to high-quality palliative and hospice care services for individuals and their families.

So far, our discussion has touched upon key aspects in the care journey—advance care planning, caregiver roles and duties, delivery reform, and professional engagement—mostly at the federal level. But, clearly, states also have a role to play in improving advanced illness care.

State Innovation

Using local community groups and resources, states are in a better position to tailor public policy and implement more custom delivery reforms that can have an even greater impact on families at the point of care. This is accomplished through a closer, in-depth monitoring of the specific needs of their communities. We believe a tailored approach to the federal Policy Agenda outlined above can be customized to states based on their needs, current resources available, demographics, and geographic areas.

Policy Goal # 7
Support state flexibility to create and evaluate advanced care systems that may be more comprehensive, responsive and effective than current delivery systems.

We are encouraged by the sharing that is occurring between states and among regional policymakers—such as the approach being developed in Rhode Island with the assistance of Senator Sheldon Whitehouse.[91] Based on their unique profiles, states can specifically implement strategies, such as:

- Utilizing Center for Medicare and Medicaid Innovation (CMMI) grants to experiment with innovative approaches as well as participating in Medicare/Medicaid waiver programs.
- Medicare Waiver programs to expand access to care services for this population, including the Section 1115 Research & Demonstration Project allowing flexibility to test new or existing approaches to financing and delivering Medicaid and CHIP.
- Section 1915(c) Home and Community-Based Services Waivers[92] or other Medicaid home and community-based services state plan options for long-term care services in home and community

settings rather than institutional settings.

- Concurrent Section 1915(b) and 1915(c) Waivers that allows states to simultaneously implement two types of waivers to provide a continuum of services to the elderly and people with disabilities.

Next Steps

The personal stories in this chapter offer us a window into an array of systems problems and opportunities that can be addressed through effective policy and advocacy. However, they continuously bring the focus of the discussion back to the *person*. What can policy achieve to enhance the individual experience for patients, families and caregivers in a financially sustainable way? In the midst of this debate regarding policy proposals and standards of care, the focus must always remain on the person and the family.

In this chapter, we introduced the political process and the ways in which we can engage policymakers. Throughout the discussion we noted that education is a key element that policy can address for this population—education of policymakers, consumers and caregivers. Another is standardizing the scope and quality of care for this population. We need policy help to standardize metrics and create uniform advanced illness training protocols. Policy change can expand access to services and provide incentives to further engagement—whether through continued advance care planning consultations, the creation of new benefits, funding for new models, and grants to long-term care facilities and states—and do so cost-effectively. Therefore, we need to engage all stakeholders to create, implement and evaluate systems changes in care delivery and payment.

The introduction of legislative proposals and the growth of private sector programs and innovations are helping to explore new approaches to caring for this population and are paving the way for future progress. Advanced care issues are beginning to gain the recognition and credibility they deserve. Our policy and regulatory environment is changing, and stakeholders are ready to engage now and more definitely than ever before. Through our shared common experiences we can connect on a basic level and see where there are needs and gaps in care delivery systems.

We have a rare opportunity today to enter the debate fully armed with a common vision—to improve care for individuals and families. To this end, we invite all—policymakers, thought leaders, and stakeholders alike—to engage in a thorough discussion regarding what individuals, families, and caregivers need and what they receive from the system. The tool for this discussion—and for needed reform—is the C-TAC Policy Agenda created by the Coalition's Policy and Advocacy Workgroup that puts forth the necessary actions (see www.thectac.org for more details.)

By elevating the issue among the broader stakeholder community, actively engaging and informing policymakers and focusing our efforts on the key issues that individuals and families experience at the ground level, we are able to move down a clear path for policy reform.

SECTION III

ACTION STEPS:
TAKING THINGS FORWARD

CHAPTER 7

Setting Priorities
Nancy Brown and Jennie Chin Hansen

"'Would you tell me, please, which way I ought to go from here?'
'That depends a good deal on where you want to get to,' said the Cat.
'I don't much care where—' said Alice.
'Then it doesn't matter which way you go,' said the Cat."

—Lewis Carroll, from Alice's Adventures in Wonderland

Throughout this book we have made the case for transforming advanced illness care from our current splintered health care system that too often fails to deliver the care that patients and their families want and need to one that delivers seamless, person-centered, coordinated care regardless of the setting. In Section 1, we discussed the current state of advanced illness care in America and concluded that because of the work by many people, we now have an opportunity to build on that solid foundation to take a great leap forward in providing the quality care that people want and deserve. In Section 2, we looked closely at the elements of reform. We defined what it means and what it takes to provide care that truly puts patients and families first. We delved into the role of spirituality and the role of employers in helping both patients and caregivers deal with the economic and emotional demands of advanced care. We looked at the best-practice care models—the people who are getting it right—to determine what they have in common and what it would take to implement those models in more communities across the country. Finally, we looked at the role of public policy and advocacy in transforming the system.

Clearly, even though we have made significant progress in the delivery of advanced illness care over the past several decades, much work remains to be done. In this section, we will summarize and specify the priority areas where action is needed to truly transform advanced illness care. That means care delivered based on an informed and shared decision-making process involving evidence, clinicians' expertise, and patients'/families' wishes and goals. The objective is to achieve quality care delivered at the right time and in the right setting as guided by patients and their families, with input from clinicians, families/caregivers, and spiritual advisors. As Diane Meier, MD, Director of the Center to Advance Palliative Care (CAPC), has noted, "It's about creating a system of care that enables patients' wishes to actually be honored.[93]

"Make the right way the easy way."

—Richard Payne, M.D., Duke Divinity School
National Summit on Advanced Illness Care, Washington, DC
January 29-30, 2013

Overcoming Barriers

In order to "make the right way the easy way," we must eliminate a number of barriers that prevent people from receiving the type of quality, patient-centered care they desire and need. Many of these have been identified in previous chapters, but they can be summarized in four areas: Care delivery, health professionals, policies and consumers.

Barriers to Care Delivery

While people have a strong desire for seamless, person-centered, coordinated care, in most cases, that is not the type of care they receive. Too many patients are receiving aggressive treatment for advanced illness that is often inconsistent with their wishes. Moreover, that treatment does not always lead to better outcomes and may add unnecessarily to their costs as well as those of our health systems. Additionally, technological advances are keeping people alive, but often without regard to patients' desires or quality of life. Care is often determined more by payment mechanisms and benefits than by personal goals and patient and family wishes (along with a genuine and mutual exchange with their providers). Because health care is currently delivered in separate, loosely affiliated silos, it is inconsistent and often creates inadvertent problems in effective care. The care patients receive differs greatly depending on geographical location, the setting in which it is delivered (e.g., home, hospital, nursing home), the stage of diagnosis (e.g., early stage vs. chronic vs. terminal with chronic conditions) and the values and skills of the providers These trends not only hinder the delivery of quality care, they also create profound stress on our already strained health care system. Even worse, they are creating unnecessary emotional and financial turmoil for patients and their families as evidenced by the fact that one in four seniors lose his or her entire life's assets during the last five years of life because of the cost of care.[94]

As the number of people over 65 nearly doubles over the next two decades, this situation will only get worse, especially when we recognize that the country will face a serious shortage in family caregivers, who today provide the bulk of complex chronic care.

Yet, as the recent Institute of Medicine report, *Dying in America: Improving Quality and Honoring Individual Preferences Near the End of Life,* states, "Improving quality of care for people with advanced serious illness and a focus on their preferences may help stabilize total health care and social costs over time. In the end-of-life arena, there are opportunities for savings by avoiding acute care services that patients and families do not want and that are unlikely to benefit them.... These savings would free up funding for relevant supporting services—for example, caregiver training, nutrition services, and home safety modifications—that would ensure a better quality of life for people near the end of life and protect and support their families."[95]

Barriers Confronting Health Professionals

Clinicians, especially physicians and nurses, are trained primarily in acute care settings with an intense focus on administering tests and procedures. Although an increasing number of medical residents have rotations through hospice, this is often insufficient to counter the impulse to "do something." Patients and families are also inculcated with the belief that there is always something more that can be done. Understanding that the patient may derive greater benefit from pulling back on tests and interventions is an educational challenge for both patients and clinicians.

Additionally, it is still rare that health professionals truly seek to understand "what matters" to the person vs. what is the matter with them, which would guide the planning of care in a very different manner, leading to genuine "person centeredness." The culture of giving care TO people blunts the reflective exchange that should actually guide the care that is mutually understood and agreed to. These trends are not only hindering the delivery of quality care, they also are creating profound stress. There is very little in health professionals' education that has promoted this form of first listening with reflective inquiry before "doing to" the person.

Clinicians generally also are not taught enough about working effectively in multidisciplinary teams; yet, team approaches are a hallmark of good palliative and well managed complex care and essential to managing transitions and avoiding re-hospitalization.[96] Likewise, clinicians, especially physicians, report feeling unprepared when facing difficult questions on how and when to share information with patients and families. They need help in learning how to communicate uncertainty. (For example, physicians generally greatly overestimate a patient's survival prospects). Additionally, chaplains, other clergy, and other professionals from whom patients and families seek advice may also need special training to participate effectively in and normalize conversations around advanced illness care. The bottom line is that we must help retrain our current providers both in skill and leadership, as well as assure this becomes part of the core competency of trainees in all appropriate disciplines.

Policy Barriers

There is no question that current political gridlock in Washington makes forward progress difficult on complex and potentially controversial issues such as advanced illness care. Nevertheless, we must pursue legislative and regulatory reform, because current policies place significant barriers on efforts to improve care. As stated previously, health care delivery for Americans with advanced illness is fragmented, with little coordination, support or regard for personal wishes. Care options are determined more by various payment mechanisms and benefits rather than by the personal goals of individuals, families and caregivers. Public payment systems are misaligned with misplaced incentives that promote and reward quantity of care over quality of care. The current fee-for-service payment method does not encourage efficient use of services or proper care coordination and accountable use of evidence. It also lacks the concepts of shared risk and shared accountability. Delivery of care and reimbursement mechanisms are confined to separate, uncoordinated, and loosely affiliated silos. Thus, treatment coverage is often unreasonable for the circumstances and does not promote either informed choice or high quality; nor frankly does it provide the vital, non-medical services (e.g., supportive assistance in the home, nourishment or transportation services) that are actually needed to help maintain functional stability and to help avoid destabilization which often leads to the use of institutional (e.g., emergency room, hospital) care. This makes it difficult to deliver cost-efficient care across all settings. While the Medicare hospice benefit was a major step forward in the provision of quality advanced illness care, today's eligibility rules, as dictated by Medicare, limit access to the supportive care that would be useful to many people. Finally, while employee caregivers struggle to meet the challenges of working and providing advanced care to loved ones, their employers are hampered by a lack of widely accepted best practices and resources for providing support.

Barriers for Consumers

A common language of health and medical terms is lacking among patients, families and caregivers, and even among health professionals who often assign different meanings and interpretation to the same words. This lack of common terminology is a critical, multilayered problem that cuts across and within population segments. Consumers are also hampered by limited health literacy and a lack of understanding as to how payment rules can impact what type and level of care is provided. This leaves them unable to make critical choices and informed decisions. For example, because many consumers are unaware of care options, they do not initiate communication with health care professionals regarding plans of care and prognosis. And, physicians typically do not initiate any discussion of options until very late in the course of an illness, if at all. The problem is compounded by the fact that many consumers are not aware of many of the common problems that individuals, families and caregivers face during advanced illness, so they don't plan or prepare for those situations, nor do they have knowledge themselves of many of the social services and supports that already exist in the community.

Priority Focus Areas—What Must Be Done

> *"We must act."*
>
> —Judith Salerno, M.D., formerly with the Institute of Medicine,
> now President, Susan B. Komen Foundation
> National Summit on Advanced Illness Care, Washington, DC, January 29-30, 2013

Overcoming the challenges of ensuring that everyone has access to high-quality advanced illness care requires an integrated effort across four focus areas. This is where we need to establish clear priorities, create action steps, and implement.

1. Analyze and spread the adoption of best-practice clinical delivery models that ensure high-quality, coordinated care across all settings.
2. Engage and support clinicians and other health professionals to adopt innovative tools and techniques that result in appropriate care and effective shared decision making with patients and their families.
3. Develop, monitor and advocate for public and private policies to support and improve advanced illness care.
4. Build public knowledge and engagement to help people make informed decisions and support changes in public policy and in the advanced care delivery system.

Priorities for Best-Practice Clinical Models

As noted in Chapter 5, advanced illness care can be structured in many different ways, but it order to be most effective, it should adhere to seven important principles:

1. Having an accurate definition of the population needing advanced illness care.
2. Personal goals should drive care, not just clinical needs.
3. A well-designed care program doesn't just coordinate care, it also integrates care settings to create a true system of care that has as its objective the best stability and well-being for the person and family.
4. Effective advance care planning would occur over time with the identification of values, goals and expectations and the understanding that reassessments would be deployed as changes develop.
5. Advanced illness care is customized for each person and can evolve into a mix of curative, restorative and palliative care.
6. Plans and providers of advanced illness care need to leverage systemic, structural innovation and provide the support for this significant cultural shift.
7. Advanced illness care must include constructive messaging and engagement that demonstrate the benefit that ensues when "best care comes together to support the best well-being of the person."

As noted in Chapter 5, many advanced care plans and providers are beginning to incorporate these principles into advanced care models that are proving valuable to patients and their families, providers and health plans. The challenge is to apply them on a wider scale—to make them standard for advanced illness care across the country so all people can receive the best advanced illness care available.

To meet this challenge, as noted in Chapter 5, C-TAC and America's Health Insurance Plan Foundation's Institute for Health Systems Solutions (IHSS) launched The Advanced Care Project. This is an initiative among various health care stakeholders—health plans, employers, health systems, faith-based and other leaders—to identify, analyze and compare best practice clinical care models for advanced illness care management and to promote the results of this work to health care systems and other health care system participants across the United States.

The first phase engaged experts to: Identify appropriate models; analyze areas of similarities and differences; assess their significance in terms of effectiveness, replication and scalability; and establish a best practices framework (see Chapter 5).

This work is now completed, and a report is now available at www. thectac.org. Further information and analysis will emerge from testing the framework among care systems in a variety of settings. In addition, C-TAC's Policy Agenda will be revised to ensure that policies favorable to best practices will be pursued at national and state levels.

The goal of this next phase of the Advanced Care Project is to strengthen the evidence base for advanced illness care. Experts will collect and analyze additional data based on common metrics from a representative sample of providers, health plans, and others, operating in different geographic and environmental settings.

The final—and perhaps most challenging—phase of the project will be to plan, promote, and support the implementation of the best practices framework in health systems and practices across the country. The goal is nothing less than to ensure more compassionate, person-centered and effective advanced illness care for all.

Priorities for Professional Engagement and Support

As medical professionals seek to provide the best care for their seriously ill patients, they grapple with difficult questions on how and when to share information with patients, families and even with their fellow professionals.[97] This challenge is further complicated by the fact that "communicating bad news" (along with "improving pain control") is difficult, and one of the most requested topics for physician training programs on advanced illness/end-of-life care.

Physicians are a trusted source of information for patients and their families, but they need not be the primary focal point for supporting patient and surrogate decision-making.[98] Advanced illness care programs that also involve physician assistants, nurse practitioners and other professionals have shown great potential for improving care by integrating decision-making support as a natural element of patient-centered care.

Conversations and decision-making around advanced illness care are most successful for patients, families, caregivers, and the advanced care team when they involve an informed professional care team that removes barriers, manages expectations and provides resources and planning tools to use before the onset of advanced illness.

The key to integrating shared decision making into advanced illness care is to first gain a more comprehensive understanding of how clinicians, patients and families make care and treatment decisions, and then to determine how informed and shared decision making among all those in advanced care decisions can be improved. To tackle this issue, C-TAC, along with The Advisory Board Company, created the Shared Decision Making Project. Their research uncovered a number of important findings, which may lead to better integration of shared decision making in advanced illness care.

As stated earlier, there is no common language of health and medical terms in advanced illness. This is not only a problem among patients, families and caregivers; it is also a problem among health professionals, who often assign different meanings and interpretations to the same words. For example, while efforts are underway to distinguish "palliative care" from "end-of-life" and "hospice care," many physicians believe that palliative care is end-of-life care, offered only when curative attempts are no longer viable. As a result, these physicians might be unwilling to refer a patient still undergoing curative treatment to a palliative care specialist.

Likewise, because people generally have little awareness or understanding of topics around advanced illness (e.g., 78 percent do not know what palliative care is[99]), considerable miscommunication often occurs between clinicians and patients and their families. For example, when a physician tells a patient that a treatment has "X percent likelihood of success," she presumably means that X percent of the time the desired medical outcome is achieved—say, three more months of remission for a cancer patient. But the patient hearing "X percent chance of success" may interpret "success" as a cure and a lifetime free of disease.

Without clear communication, consumers cannot accurately tell providers what they want. Moreover, they often don't even know what to ask for. Likewise, if clinicians do not correctly interpret the request, they cannot translate it into patient-centered care.

Consumers gain an understanding of their health care from their experiences and the emotional bonds formed with their physicians. Strategies that connect directly with those experiences and emotions may be effective in bridging communication gaps. To that end, consumers want information to be presented in positive ways.[100] They do not want to hear horror stories, problems or what happens without advance planning. They tend to look ahead and are interested in better health care and supportive communities to help them live as healthy and independently as they can.

Clearly, we need to continue to build the evidence base to better understand what works and what doesn't, and we need to develop standards for clinician-patient (and family) communications that will lead to effective, shared decision making. These standards should be tied to reimbursement, licensing and credentialing of clinicians. That means we also must ensure that appropriate professional education and development opportunities are available for all clinicians who care for individuals with advanced illness, and that resources are available to increase the number of clinicians with palliative care training.

The culture of our health system does not always foster or promote needed competencies for appropriate patient-family/clinician decision making; nonetheless, there are tested, quality training resources available that improve clinician training and patient/family outcomes. Yet, many clinicians are not accessing these tools and/or need additional training in communication and interpersonal skills to provide person-centered care for advanced illness. We must do more to raise awareness of existing innovative tools and solutions in clinician support and training and do more to increase training for the delivery of community-based care.

Improving clinician training requires reorienting advanced illness care by placing the patient and family at the center of the care. That also means redesigning the specific workflows, roles, and tools in the health system and empowering champions within health care systems to advocate for transformation.

Finally, we must develop and promote training protocols for medical and other education curricula for the variety of health professionals caring for individuals with advanced illness with federal, state, and private-sector stakeholders (including updates to continuing education certifications). By doing so, we can ensure a stable, competent, vibrant and compassionate workforce encouraging interdisciplinary collaboration with patients, their families, and their caregivers. At the same time, we must work with federal, state, and private-sector stakeholders to attract more professionals to the health care workforce with expanded roles and responsibilities unique to advanced illness care delivery.

Priorities for Policy & Advocacy

Effective policies (public and private) and policy advocacy are essential to overcome barriers in current law (described earlier in this chapter) that hinder the delivery of higher-quality advanced illness care. Legislative and regulatory change is also needed both at federal and state levels to advance the other strategies for transforming advanced illness care (public engagement, models that work, professional education and support). In Chapter 6, we identified seven public policy goals for improving advanced illness care. These are:

1. Normalize advance care planning through counseling and meaningful discussion of prognosis, goals of care, personal values and treatment preferences.
2. Build health information technologies that promote advance care

planning documentation and effective information sharing across time, place and provider with appropriate safeguards for privacy.

3. Ensure a full range of supports and services to caregivers and families facing advanced illness.

4. Ensure person-centered care management that effectively bridges acute, post-acute, and long-term care settings, treatment and time.

5. Support expanded research as a key tool to improve care delivery practices and strengthen quality standards for individuals and families facing advanced illness.

6. Build a health care workforce educated and equipped with the clinical and social skills to enable people with advanced illness and their families and caregivers to navigate their treatment, care, and support options according to their values and preferences.

7. Support state flexibility to create and evaluate advanced care systems that may be more comprehensive, responsive and effective than current delivery systems.

We must work on multiple fronts to achieve these policy goals. The following areas are critical:

- **Individual care planning** including counseling, discussion of choices, social supports, and support of family and caregivers. This requires trained professionals familiar with these needs and the formalization of processes incorporating physicians, nurses, social workers and others with the expertise to best support individuals with advanced illness and their families;

- **Consumer and family caregiver education**, information and support including the creation and promotion of publicly available resources; personnel to help individuals with advanced illness and their families and caregivers navigate the health system with more independence, confidence, and comfort; as well as access to the vital long-term social services and supports available in the community to support patients, families, and caregivers across the care continuum;

- **Quality standards** including mechanisms and protocols to ensure delivery of high-quality advanced illness care and support as a nationally accepted standard of care;

- **Professional education** including development of protocols, training programs, and re-training support systems to promote a health care workforce with the clinical and social skills and competencies to appropriately care for people with advanced illness and to support families and caregivers;

- **Payment and Regulatory Reform** including payment models and incentives to expand options for care coordination, care transitions, and care management services that pursue integration of services across the dimensions of time, space, and treatment;

- **Health and health information technology** including developing standards, protocols, and incentives to ensure a modern, quality, efficient delivery system for individuals with advanced illness across settings and providers in order to improve communication among providers, individuals, emergency, inpatient, home and community-based services and family caregivers and to ensure more efficient integration between "silos" of services; and

- **Research** to improve care delivery practices and clinical standards for individuals with advanced illness.

C-TAC, its members and others are working closely with congressional leaders on a bipartisan, bicameral basis, as well as with the administration to raise awareness and to support federal and also state-level policy efforts. To guide these advocacy initiatives, C-TAC developed a Policy Framework that describes the barriers in current law and now has created a comprehensive Policy Agenda that will help guide and direct federal and state advocacy initiatives across the country (see Chapter 6).

Priorities for Building Public Engagement

Building public engagement to help people make informed decisions and to support changes in advanced illness care delivery systems and policies is essential to transforming advanced illness care in America. Patients, their families and caregivers crave information about serious illness and how to navigate the environment to achieve the best outcomes. Yet, many are unaware of where to turn for help when they need care, what advanced illness care services are available in their communities, and which services are covered by Medicare or insurance. Research shows, for instance, that many people are unaware of the services hospice provides, how and when to access these services and how they are financed.[101] They are also unaware of the many social services and supports that already exist in the community.

As a result, many do not initiate communication with health care professionals regarding plans of care and prognosis. Communication is transactional rather than part of a well thought-out, longer range plan. This problem is compounded by a low awareness of many of the common problems that individuals, families and caregivers face during advanced illness and the subsequent lack of personal care planning to prepare for those situations.

A number of important national and regional initiatives (e.g., The Conversation Project and Honoring Choices in Minneapolis/St. Paul) are at work building public will for change and empowering people to make informed plans and decisions for advanced illness. These initiatives, including C-TAC's, are often focused on (1) encouraging families and individuals to have discussions about anticipated life course changes and challenges and to document those discussions before the likely emergencies occur and (2) educating people about specific care options along the advanced illness continuum. As with efforts to engage and support professionals, these efforts are hampered by the lack of a common language, lack of a clear understanding of values and preferences and a lack of shared decision making. Family caregivers are too often peripheral to the formal treatment of the ill person and excluded from the process of decision-making. Finally, there is no baseline against which to measure progress in public engagement initiatives.

Transforming the interaction among patients, families, caregivers and providers is a two-way street. The common language must be common to all, not just among professionals and not just among patients, families and caregivers. Likewise, shared decisions must be shared by all, which means all people involved in the care must be involved in the decision-making process.

In addition to the Shared Decision-Making Project described earlier in this chapter, C-TAC has developed CareJourney.org—a consumer-based website aimed at helping patients, their families and caregivers understand their diagnoses, what they mean for the future, and how to plan for their care and caregiving—medical, financial, emotional and spiritual. The information on CareJourney.org comes from C-TAC member organizations and is well documented and carefully crafted.

Additionally, a number of innovative and interactive resources are available for training and leadership in health systems, hospitals and physician groups, including those from the Center to Advance Palliative Care (CAPC).

C-TAC's alliance of faith leaders is also piloting a community-based model to improve the quality of life for patients with advanced illness and for family caregivers. The goal of this *Interfaith Initiative* is to extend and strengthen the health care delivery system, improve outcomes for people with advanced illness, reduce the burden on caregivers and reinforce community support for advanced illness care (see Chapter 3).

Measuring Results

> *"What gets measured gets done, what gets measured and fed back gets done well, what gets rewarded gets repeated."*
>
> - John E. Jones
> (author of New Supervisor Training)

Transforming advanced illness care from its current state to one that truly delivers and rewards person-centered care may appear daunting, but history teaches us that it can be done. Over the past fifty years, Americans have experienced significant improvements in survival rates associated with diseases such as coronary artery disease and several forms of cancer. Moreover, dramatic improvements in quality have occurred in other industries such as the American automobile industry and the commercial aviation industry. These improvements have not been the result of random chance or mere technology enhancements. Rather, they are founded on systematic approaches based on proven principles.[102]

In the health care arena, the concept of performance measurement is still evolving, and we must be alert to unintended consequences when measures are selected. Metrics for hospital-related care processes, including in-hospital mortality, infection rates, medications administered, length of stay and readmission rates are readily available at federal and some state and commercial websites (e.g., www.medicare.gov/hospitalcompare[103]). However, individual physician and group practice measures have lagged behind those on hospital performance. Thanks to CMS' Physician Quality Reporting System[104] and several private insurers, they are beginning to catch up. Likewise, the Center for Medicare and Medicaid Innovation (CMMI) and the Patient Centered Outcomes Research Institute (PCORI) are leading efforts to develop quality measures across sites of care and for various conditions. This is largely the result of the movement towards value-based payments, which can reward or penalize providers based at least in part on their performance on a defined set of quality measures. Progress will increasingly lead to measures that come from a patient and family perspective in support of achieving the Triple Aim in health care—to improve patient experience of care (including quality and safety), to improve the health of populations, and to reduce costs of care. All of this provides the opportunity to develop measures focused on advanced illness management.[105]

So, if "what gets measured gets done," what dimensions of advanced illness care should be measured? Initially, there should be attention to four dimensions of care.

1. Quality

Any assessment of advanced illness care must focus on safety and quality measures, such as adherence to established guidelines for care, mortality rates and utilization of resources (e.g., length of stay, re-hospitalization rates, emergency department visits). Measures on quality provide information on whether advanced illness care is improving patient outcomes, inclusive of the patients' perspective, and are also necessary to ensure that any streamlining or efficiencies achieved through policy, practice or payment innovations do not result in adverse outcomes. Several studies show that approximately one-third of health care spending in the U.S. is "wasteful" and in many cases could have adverse effects on individuals through care delivery failures, lack of care coordination, and overtreatment.[106] A recent study in the *New England Journal of Medicine* (NEJM) on advanced lung cancer indicated that less aggressive medical intervention coupled with effective palliative care produced greater patient well-being, less depression and greater longevity.[107]

2. Access

Measures related to access to the continuum of care, ranging from health and wellness care through hospice care, are also essential for improving health care performance. Currently, impressions about access to care are inferred from data that document disparities in health care outcomes associated with race, ethnicity, poverty or "all of the above." We must continue to focus on these communities, to ensure that all Americans receive high-quality health care that meets their wishes and honors their dignity. Additional measures that reflect personal experience of those with advanced illness are needed as well. Such personal experiences will highlight the gaps between provider and consumer perceptions of care. Studies suggest that this gap in "person centeredness" is quite substantial and often unrecognized by providers who may not consider the vital role of the person's support system or whether an individual lacks one (lives alone without a network).

3. Patient-centeredness

Measures of person-centeredness should include those of family, designated surrogate and caregivers, all of whom are the focus of comprehensive advanced illness care. Topics should include perceptions of shared decision-making, access to medical and related social resources (e.g., care at home, respite), care coordination, pain and symptom management. These are essential to identifying areas where progress is needed and for disseminating documented improvement strategies nationally. Several of these measures are now being initiated in the Consumer Assessments of Healthcare Providers and Systems (CG-CAHPS; https://cahps.ahrq.gov). This approach will begin to shine a light on this often-neglected area of health care delivery. The first reports of this work will begin emerging in 2015. The lack of prior attention to patient-centeredness has created a major impediment to implementing performance improvement in this most fundamental area of health care delivery. A national survey of consumer perceptions related to patient-centeredness is required to provide a benchmark of current status and catalyze performance improvement in this area.

4. Cost

Cost data are currently captured for the Medicare population, which includes not only those over age 65 but also for those with certain chronic or debilitating diseases (e.g., kidney failure requiring dialysis, those receiving at least two years of Social Security Disability Insurance benefits, or those with amyotrophic lateral sclerosis). Although Medicare alone does not encompass the totality of those with chronic illness, it accounts for a great number and its population is supplemented by data from such sources as Hospital Compare and Physician Compare. Together, these will provide a window of observation into the efficiency of care delivery. Using Medicare data, the Dartmouth Atlas, prepared by the Dartmouth Institute, provides a vision of what might be expected from regular monitoring of cost and resource utilization.[108]

The system of measurement across each of these dimensions should use existing measures of process, outcome or patient/family satisfaction whenever relevant to reduce duplication and reporting burden on providers and to provide a longitudinal history of progress. In other cases, however, new and meaningful measures on quality of life will need to be developed in areas that are important but not traditionally measured. This requires a transparent, consensus-based approach with a respected endorsement authority such as the National Quality Forum (NQF).[109] We will perhaps need a body of fewer but more meaningful measures as we launch into this arena of advanced illness care.

The National Quality Strategy (NQS; http://www.ahrq.gov/workingforquality) provides the framework for this work. It envisions three overarching goals: Better Care, Healthy People and Communities, and Affordable Care. In alignment with the goals of the NQS, NQF (through the Measure Applications Partnership) is constructing families of measures that allow stakeholders to identify the most relevant measures for a given need. Not only does this tool allow stakeholders to focus on the most important measures in a given area, it also promotes alignment across measurement programs.[110] Areas where families of measures exist—and that can be leveraged to assess advanced illness care—include specific common diseases such as cardiovascular disease or diabetes, and more general delivery principles such as care coordination, access to hospice care, person- and family-centered care, affordability, population health and patient safety, especially among vulnerable populations such as dual eligible beneficiaries.

Examples of Advanced Illness Care Measures: Building on the Existing Foundation

Advanced illness care will vary among individuals depending on factors such as socioeconomic needs, age, personal preferences, family support, diagnosis and severity of illness. Further, clinicians and health systems are hesitant to implement new quality measures due to the plethora of existing ones. However, opportunities exist to select a limited number of specific measures from within 'families' of measures, thus reducing redundancy and unnecessary inefficiencies and allowing the basic tenets of advanced illness care to be measured across four key dimensions. Some examples might include:

1. **Quality**
   - Hospital admissions and length of stay
   - ICU length of stay
   - Emergency department visits
   - Disease specific process and outcome measures, such as heart failure, chronic obstructive pulmonary disease, or advanced cancers
   - Care coordination (e.g., transitions of care at time of discharge)
   - Pain and symptom management
   - JCAHO accreditation for Advanced Certification in Disease-specific Care

2. **Access**
   - Percent of individuals in a health system with advance directives, or POLST
   - Enrollment in palliative or hospice care
   - Home health utilization

3. **Patient-centeredness**
   - Percent of time treatment was consistent with care plan
   - Patient and family satisfaction
   - Site of care at death (e.g., home, extended care, hospital, ICU)
   - Provider engagement in shared decision making

---

4. **Cost**
   - Resource utilization (diagnostic imaging, laboratory tests, medications)
   - Cost-per-case-per day in hospital or post-acute care
   - Total expenditures in last 12-24 months or less of life

Achievement of the NQS goals is consistent with the goals of advanced illness care. As in most scenarios the real accomplishment of these goals lies not in lofty language or vision, but rather in the front-line work of providers, patients, caregivers and families that must translate from rhetoric to action. Such translation will require consistent application, measurement and refinement that will help shed light on what works and what needs to be changed. This is the basis for what many call "the learning health system," a term that currently seems more a vision than a reality. Such learning will inform health care leaders, payers, policy makers and regulators, all of whom will be far more likely to act based on evidence rather than argument.

In summary, the broad implementation of efficient metrics that assess current status and future progress in health care delivery is essential for accelerating the adoption of successful advanced illness care. They are needed to empower consumers, to motivate providers, to eliminate health care disparities and to guide and influence policy makers and regulators to shape a system that truly meets the needs of all, especially as we face the onslaught of the burden of illness inevitably associated with an aging population. There are glimmers of hope already; these can be ignited by passion, but they must be informed by metrics that guide rational behavior and decision-making.

John E. Jones was right. "What gets measured gets done, what gets measured and fed back gets done well, what gets rewarded gets repeated."

Conclusion

We must transform advanced illness care in America by empowering consumers, changing the health delivery system, aligning our expertise to the hopes and wishes of the public, advocating for more effective public and private policies and enhancing provider and family care partner training and capacity. By implementing these priorities, we can achieve this goal. We have to pursue these priorities with a multi-faceted approach, and we have to realize that change will not happen all at once, nor will it be consistent. That's why we have to engage with many change agents at all levels: heath systems and providers, payers, spiritual leaders, patients, families and care partners and other stakeholders to drive change.

Over the next two decades, the number of people 65 and older will nearly double to more than 72 million, or one in five Americans. Most people with advanced illness will be in this age group. Without change, they will be at higher risk for unnecessary hospitalizations and unwanted treatment, adverse drug reactions, pain and suffering and conflicting medical advice. All of this will result in higher cost of care to families (both economically and emotionally) and to the nation. We cannot accept this as inevitable. We must do better; there is too much at stake for a healthy, civil and compassionate nation. Let's enact a sensible system that is ethical, accountable and respectful and that isn't overly medicalized when "best care" is at stake.

CHAPTER 8

A Call to Action
Bill Novelli and Tom Koutsoumpas

"Yesterday is not ours to recover, but tomorrow is ours to win or lose."
—Lyndon Baines Johnson

As we continue the great task of transforming advanced illness care in America, let's agree that this issue is more about life than it is about death. In his book, *Being Mortal: Medicine and What Matters in the End*, Atul Gawande, MD, writes about those with advanced illness having a deep need for everyday comforts, for companionship, and achieving modest aims; as he puts it, [we need] "to be the authors of our lives."[111] He discusses the story of his daughter's piano teacher whose final wish was to continue giving lessons for the last months of her life despite her terminal illness. After returning home from the hospital, she enrolled in hospice care, and was able to focus on giving piano lessons – greatly improving her quality-of-life in her final stages of illness.

A friend and college classmate of Bill's wrote about the final year of her partner's life. She titled it, *Coordinated Health Care: Who's in Charge?* She wrote:

> *"Here is a list of specialists he had to go to see regularly: head and neck surgeons (four in the same practice), medical oncologist, radiation oncologist, cardiologist, urologist, dermatologist, gastroenterologist, internist, two integrated medicine MDs, dentist, speech and swallowing therapist, and*

lymphoma therapist...and visits with a pulmonary surgeon, plastic surgeon, oral surgeon, ophthalmologist and palliative care specialist.

We thought the integrated care MDs or the internal medicine MD would be more involved in the coordination, but even they were focused on their individual contributions. Throughout the year, there were massive numbers of prescription drugs, ordered at two different pharmacies, many of which had to be in liquid form, crushable, or powdered, some requiring pre-certification from the insurance company, taking days and even weeks to complete.

I now look at the entirety of his medical history as a series of hurricanes that hit him, which he survived because his immune system, like the levies in New Orleans, held. Finally the storm, like Katrina, was too strong, the aging process weakened him, and the levies broke."

Stories like these are all too familiar to us. You've read others like them in this book, and undoubtedly you either have a similar story yourself, or know someone who does.

The point of this book is to say—and to help us all realize—that it doesn't have to be that way. *There is a path forward.* We know what has to be done to transform advanced illness care in America so that all people who are seriously ill receive the right care at the right time in the right place, to empower patients and their families and honor their dignity.

The path forward begins by putting patients and families first, ensuring that their values and preferences are taken into account every step of the way, and that these values and preferences drive clinical and treatment decisions. By doing that, we will stop regarding people as a set of medical conditions that need to be treated, and instead see them as whole persons with minds and bodies and souls and families and friends and values and purpose that make them who they are. Suzanne Mintz, a family care advocate, views patients and their caregivers as a single unit of care that [reflects] "the interwoven nature of their relationship."

We can then connect people's medical needs with their spiritual needs and develop treatment plans that embrace both, while valuing the dignity and sanctity of human life. Rabbi Richard Address and Rev. Dr. Tyrone

Pitts said it well in Chapter 3: "Families and individuals who face the challenges associated with advanced illness often come to the reality that, while no 'cure' may be found; it is possible to be 'healed.'" As we are learning from our work with African American and Latino churches in Alameda County, California, incorporating clergy and spiritual leaders into the interdisciplinary care team can provide a person and a family with a sense of acceptance and peace. Despite their physical condition and lack of a cure, people seek spiritual healing. In short, it helps both the person and the family live in the face of death.

In order to succeed in closing the gap between the care people with advanced illness want and what they currently receive, we need to implement policies and practices that support person-centered care, shared decision-making with patients and families and interdisciplinary care teams. We have made significant progress over the years in these areas. Employers are beginning to see the value in developing policies and practices to support employees who are also caregivers, as well as employees with advanced care needs. The Medicare Hospice Benefit (created in 1982 and made permanent in 1986), and more recently, several provisions contained in the Affordable Care Act have paved the way for current efforts to transform advanced illness care and will play a critical role in shaping the transformation.

We see the impact of these policies in various health systems and in communities across the country. For example, Diane Meier, MD and director of the Center to Advance Palliative Care at Mount Sinai School of Medicine, has made substantial progress in promoting and implanting palliative care units in hospitals and other settings on a national basis. And as evidenced in Chapter 5, many health systems and providers throughout the country are innovating and implementing new practices and procedures to transform advanced illness care in their communities with great success. We are now positioned to take a giant leap forward; we're only just beginning.

Reaching the policy goals identified in Chapter 6 will require bold, coordinated advocacy on the part of everyone interested in transforming advanced care. While it will be difficult, the time is right to tackle it and build on the solid foundation we already have. Here's why:

- The aging of the 78 million baby boom generation will demand it. This feisty group is coming face-to-face with advanced illness issues as caregivers for their aging parents and as they face their own mortality. They will want a better system for themselves.
- Perhaps related to the aging baby boomers is an apparent interest among the public to talk and think more about these issues. There is increasing coverage in the media. Ellen Goodman, who founded The Conversation Project, believes that the first place for these conversations is at the kitchen table. She calls for a willingness to talk as individuals, as families and as a culture about what we want for when, as they say, the time comes.
- We now have an evidence-base of solutions that work. Chapter 5 contains numerous examples of health systems that have devised new principles of care that are yielding positive results both for providers and for patients and families.
- Members of Congress from both sides of the aisle see the need. Whenever we talk to them, they start with their own powerful stories – about their mothers, fathers and other loved ones. There is no partisanship in any of this, and when we offer solutions and show them what is working, they listen.

The Institute of Medicine's recent comprehensive report, *Dying in America: Improving Quality and Honoring Individual Preferences Near the End of Life*, offered five key recommendations:

1. Government health insurers and care delivery programs, as well as private health insurers, should cover the provision of comprehensive care for individuals with advanced serious illness who are nearing the end of life.
2. Professional societies and other organizations that establish

quality standards should develop standards for clinician-patient communication and advance care planning that are measurable, actionable, and evidence based. These standards should change as needed to reflect the evolving population and health system needs and be consistent with emerging evidence, methods, and technologies. Payers and health care delivery organizations should adopt these standards and their supporting processes, and integrate them into assessments, care plans, and the reporting of health care quality. Payers should tie such standards to reimbursement, and professional societies should adopt policies that facilitate tying the standards to reimbursement, licensing, and credentialing.

3. Educational institutions, credentialing bodies, accrediting boards, state regulatory agencies, and health care delivery organizations should establish the appropriate training, certification, and/or licensure requirements to strengthen the palliative care knowledge and skills of all clinicians who care for individuals with advanced serious illness who are nearing the end of life.

4. Federal, state, and private insurance and health care delivery programs should integrate the financing of medical and social services to support the provision of quality care consistent with the values, goals, and informed preferences of people with advanced serious illness nearing the end of life. To the extent that additional legislation is necessary to implement this recommendation, the administration should seek and Congress should enact such legislation. In addition, the federal government should require public reporting on quality measures, outcomes, and costs regarding care near the end of life (e.g., in the last year of life) for programs it funds or administers (e.g., Medicare, Medicaid, the Department of Veterans Affairs). The federal government should encourage all other payment and health care delivery systems to do the same.

5. Civic leaders, public health and other governmental agencies, community-based organizations, faith-based organizations,

consumer groups, health care delivery organizations, payers, employers, and professional societies should engage their constituents and provide fact-based information about care of people with advanced serious illness to encourage advance care planning and informed choice based on the needs and values of individuals.[112]

The IOM report is a blueprint for reform. The report's recommendations are aligned with the priorities we set forth in Chapter 7. The IOM report concludes: "a patient-centered, family-oriented approach to care near the end of life should be a high national priority and...compassionate, affordable, and effective care for these patients is an achievable goal."[113] That's right on target, and as Victor Dzau, MD, president of the IOM, emphasized, "The time is now."[114]

At C-TAC, our role as a nonpartisan and nonprofit coalition is that of a convener and catalyst. Our job is to support and bring together people and organizations that are doing the hard work of reforming advanced illness care in America. We see public engagement, promoting best-practice clinical models, supporting clinicians and other health professionals and policy advocacy as key priorities for this movement.

In 2013, we held our first National Summit on Advanced Illness Care, and we convened another in 2015. There has been a lot of progress to report, but a tremendous amount is still undone. The bottom line, the great goal, is that: *all Americans with advanced illness, especially the sickest and most vulnerable, will receive comprehensive, high-quality, person-and family-centered care that is consistent with their goals and values and honors their dignity.* We presume you are reading this book because this great goal is important to you. So please join us in this effort.

The way we see it, the mortality rate in America is still 100 percent. None of us are going to come out of this alive anyhow, so we might as well get this done!

APPENDIX A

A Brief History of Advanced Illness Care in America
Boe Workman and Jay Mahoney

The concept of self-determined care dates back to 1914, when case law established the requirement to obtain a patient's consent for invasive medical procedures. But it wasn't until the 1960s that the concept of self-determination began to play a large role in advanced illness care. The decade of the '60s is noted as a time of great social change and upheaval in America, fostered primarily by the civil rights movement and the anti-war movement. It was also a time that launched a movement by patient and consumer rights advocates and hospice care advocates to significantly change how society dealt with advanced illness and end-of-life care in America.

The Hospice Movement

In 1965, Florence Wald, then Dean of the Yale School of Nursing, invited British physician Dame Cicely Saunders to become a visiting faculty member at the school for the spring term. Saunders, world-renowned for her work with terminally ill patients, first applied the word "hospice"[115] to specialized care for dying patients and, in 1967, created the first hospice—St. Christopher's Hospice—in a residential suburb of London. In 1968, Wald took a sabbatical from Yale to work at St. Christopher's and learn all she could about hospice. Then, in 1974, she, along with two pediatricians and a chaplain, founded Connecticut Hospice in Branford Connecticut, the first hospice in the United States. That same year, Senators Frank Church and Frank E. Moss introduced the first hospice legislation to provide federal funds for hospice programs. Though the legislation failed, it led to a 1978 U.S. Department of Health, Education and Welfare task force that reported, "the hospice movement as a concept for the care of the terminally ill and their families is a viable concept and one which holds out a means of providing more humane care for Americans dying of terminal illness while possibly reducing costs. As such, it is the proper subject of federal support."[116] The next year, the Health Care Financing Administration (HCFA) initiated demonstration programs at 26 hospices across the country to assess the cost effectiveness of hospice care and to help determine what a hospice is and what it should provide. In 1982, Congress included a provision to create a Medicare hospice benefit in the Tax Equity and Fiscal Responsibility Act of 1982 (with a 1986 sunset provision), and in 1986, it was made permanent. States were also given the option of including hospice in their Medicaid programs, and in 1989, Congress mandated that those state payment rates be no lower than Medicare rates for hospice care. Hospice care is available to terminally ill nursing home residents, and in the Budget Reconciliation Act of 1989, Congress mandated that all states pay 95% of the states' patient-specific nursing home reimbursement rate to hospice for room and board Medicaid-eligible nursing home residents receiving hospice care. By 2011, more than 1.65 million Americans with a life-limiting illness were served by more than 5,300 hospice organizations were operating in the U.S.[117]

The progression of Hospice Care from a social experiment to becoming an integral part of the health care system is testament to the dedication, commitment and hard work of many congressional "Hospice Heroes," both members and staff, who have supported hospice care through legislation and through their deeds and words. In 1978, several years before the Medicare Hospice Benefit legislation would be introduced;

Senate icons Edward Kennedy (D-MA) and Robert Dole (R-KA) spoke enthusiastically in support of the hospice philosophy of care at one of the first National Hospice Organization (NHO) symposiums on hospice care. Years later, during the 1996 Presidential Debates, Senator Dole would reference his work on behalf of hospice as a one of the highlights of his Senate career. Congressman Leon Panetta (D-CA)—who would go on to become White House Chief of Staff under President Bill Clinton, and then Director of the CIA and Secretary of Defense under President Barack Obama— would speak with equal passion at subsequent National Hospice Organization (NHO) national meetings. Congressman Willis (Bill) Gradison (R-OH) would join Mr. Panetta on the House Ways and Means Committee in sponsoring multiple hospice specific pieces of legislation. And the list goes on: Senator Lloyd Bentsen (D-TX) in his role as Senate Finance Committee Chair and his legislative assistant, Dr. Marina L. Weiss; Ms. Bonnie Brown, Legislative Assistant to Congressman Gradison; Congressman Pete Stark (D-CA) and Ms. Sheila Burke, Chief of Staff to Senator Dole, Senator Pete Domenici (R-NM), Chairman of the Senate Budget Committee; Congressman Claude Pepper (D-FL), Chair of the Senate Select Committee on Aging and his legislative assistant, Louise Bracknell.

These "hospice heroes" however, would never have had the opportunity to achieve such status in the hospice movement if it were not for the initial work of Congressman Panetta and Senator Dole, and to the contribution of Senator John Heinz (R-PA). In December 1981, Congressman Panetta, with more than 200 co-sponsors submitted H.R. 5180, a bill to enact a Medicare Hospice Benefit by amending Title VIII of the Social Security Act. Hearings were scheduled for the bill in 1982. Companion legislation was introduced by Senator Dole, S. 1958, with more than 50 co-sponsors. No hearings were set. The Reagan Administration opposed the legislation and testified against it before the Health Sub-Committee of the House Ways and Means Committee.

In August 1982, the so-called hospice legislation was stalled and its future was at best uncertain when Congressional leaders decided to attach the legislation to the Tax Equity and Fiscal Responsibility Act of 1982 (TEFRA). Tax bills of that era were quite large so the hospice bill would attract less attention, were subject to fewer amendments and would eliminate the need to hold hospice hearings in the Senate, which at the time did not appear to be likely. The problem with such legislation is that it is vulnerable to Senate rules that allow even one Senator to object to the inclusion of a provision under the grounds that the provision is not germane to taxation. A two-thirds affirmative vote of the Senate is required to overturn the objection. There was considerable concern that such an objection would be made once the amendment made it to the Senate floor.

Even though the House of Representatives approved of the hospice language it never actually took up TEFRA, so the entire fate of the hospice legislation rested with the Senate action. As the Senate took up the tax bill, the plan was for Senator John Heinz, then Chair of the Senate Select Committee on Aging, to offer the amendment from the floor of the Senate that would add the hospice provision to the tax bill. Working his way among the mingling Senators, Senator Heinz secured sufficient votes to override any objection, which subsequently never came. Following its approval a number of Senators including Senators Dole and Heinz and future Vice President, Dan Quayle (R-IN) made statements in support of hospice care.

The adoption of the Medicare Hospice Benefit in July, 1982 represents one of the very few expansions of Medicare benefits in the nearly 50 years of Medicare's existence (until the passage of Medicare Part D in Dec. 2003), and it was accomplished by the grassroots effort of dedicated hospice advocates without the assistance of powerful lobbying firms or the contributions of political action committees. The process would form the model for more than a decade of subsequent legislative support from Congressmen Panetta and Gradison and Senators Dole and Bentsen including:

- In 1984, Public Law 98-617 increased the rate of payment for hospice routine home care services to $53.17. The standalone nature of this legislation was extraordinary at the time, and has not been achieved again in the ensuing 30-year legislative history of hospice care;

- In 1985, the Consolidated Omnibus Budget Reconciliation Act, Public Law 99-272 made the original Medicare Hospice Benefit permanent by eliminating the three-year sunset provision of that earlier legislation; increased the rates of payment for hospice services, and allowed the states to adopt a Medicaid Hospice Benefit on an optional basis;
- In 1989, Omnibus Budget Reconciliation Act , Public Law 101-239 increased hospice payments rates and directed the Secretary to increase hospice rates reflective of inflation annually, thereafter;
- In 1990, Omnibus Budget Reconciliation Act of 1990, Public Law 101-508 added a fourth, unlimited benefit period to the Medicare Hospice Benefit;
- In 1991, Department of Defense Authorization Bill, Public Law 102-172 authorized hospice care, as defined by Medicare, in military hospitals and as a CHAMPUS benefit.

Advance Directives

Another important development in the history of advanced illness care came in 1967, when a Florida attorney named Luis Kutner introduced the first living will.[118] Living wills were designed to maintain the patient's voice in medical decision-making and empower individuals to dictate the terms of their own medical care at the end of life. Initially, living wills and other forms of advance directives were simple requests to avoid medical treatment that would prolong life in undesirable conditions. As they have evolved, however, they have become increasingly specific, detailing patients' preferences for a variety of medical treatments in hypothetical medical scenarios.[119]

The first legislation to legally sanction living wills was passed in 1976 when California enacted the Natural Death Act. Within a year, forty-three states had considered living will legislation and seven states had passed bills. Advance directive legislation progressed on a state-by-state basis, and by 1982, all fifty states and the District of Columbia had passed legislation to legalize some form of advance directives.[120]

On the federal level, Congress passed the Patient Self-Determination Act (PSDA) in 1991 requiring all hospitals and health care facilities receiving Medicare or Medicaid reimbursement to determine whether patients have or wish to have an advance directive and to make an advance directive form available to those who did not have one. The PSDA did not create or legalize advance directives, instead it validated their existence in the states and acknowledged a patient's right to either refuse or accept medical treatment, safeguarding their autonomy and self-determination, protecting them against maltreatment and protecting physicians from litigation in end-of-life decision making. In 2002, the Department of Veterans Affairs launched a program to increase veterans' access to hospice and palliative care services while providing educational opportunities for clinicians in veterans' healthcare facilities. And, a provision in the 2010 Patient Protection and Affordable Care Act requires state Medicaid programs to allow children with a life-limiting illness to receive both hospice care and curative treatment.

The Role of the Courts

The courts have also played an influential role in the progression of advanced illness care. The first case to uphold advance directives involved 21-year-old Karen Ann Quinlan, who, after cardiac arrest, was resuscitated but remained in a persistent vegetative state. In 1976, the New Jersey Supreme Court granted her parents the right to withdraw life-support, holding that an individual's constitutional right to privacy outweighed the state's interest in preserving life. In writing the court's decision, Chief Justice Robert Hughes upheld four basic principles: (1) If patients are mentally unable to make treatment decisions, someone else may exercise that right for them; (2) decisions that can lead to death of a mentally incompetent patient are better made by families with the input of their doctors than by the courts; (3) decisions about end-of-life care should take into consideration both the invasiveness of the treatment involved and the likelihood of the patient's recovery; (4) patients have the right to refuse treatment even if that decision might lead to death. Ethicists and many in the medical profession interpreted the court's decision as broad enough to encompass a patient's decision to decline medical treatment under certain circumstances.

It was not until 1990 that the U.S. Supreme Court agreed to hear a case on the legality of advance directives. The case involved Nancy Cruzan, age 32, who in 1983 was involved in an automobile accident that left her in a persistent vegetative state. Years later, Cruzan's parents concluded that their daughter would never recover and that she would not have wanted to be kept alive in her current state. The hospital refused to discontinue artificial nutrition and hydration without a court order. A trial court issued the order, but the Missouri Supreme Court reversed the trial court decision on the basis that Ms. Cruzan's parents were not entitled to terminate her medical treatment in the absence of "clear and convincing evidence" that this choice reflected her wishes. A seven-year court battle reached the Supreme Court. The court ruled that, while Cruzan had the right to refuse tube feedings, the state could demand clear and convincing evidence that this was her expressed desire. They based their decision on the principle that a state may constitutionally set high barriers for decisions to withdraw food and water from incompetent patients when the patients have not spoken clearly themselves. Following the opinion of the Supreme Court, the case was sent back to the Missouri Supreme Court, which heard testimony of a verbal advance directive that was deemed to be sufficient evidence to support the refusal of medical care.

One of the most high profile court cases in recent years involved a 15-year legal battle over whether to terminate life support for Terry

Schiavo, who died in March 2005. Schiavo collapsed in her St. Petersburg, Florida home due to cardiac arrest on February 25, 1990. She suffered massive brain damage, and after two and one half months in a coma, her diagnosis was changed to vegetative state. For the next few years, doctors attempted speech and physical therapy and other experimental therapy in an attempt to return her to a state of awareness without success. In 1998, Schiavo's husband, Michael, petitioned the Sixth Circuit Court of Florida to remove her feeding tube pursuant to Florida law. Terri's parents, Robert and Mary Schindler, opposed Michael's decision and argued that she was conscious. The court determined that she would not wish to continue life-prolonging measures, and on April 24, 2001, her feeding tube was removed for the first time, only to be reinserted several days later. On February 25, 2005, a Pinellas County judge ordered the removal of Terri Schiavo's feeding tube.

Several appeals and federal government intervention followed, which included President George W. Bush returning to Washington D.C. to sign legislation (the Palm Sunday Compromise which allowed the case to be moved to a federal court) designed to keep her alive. After all attempts at appeals through the federal court system upheld the original decision to remove the feeding tube, staff at the Pinellas Park hospice facility where Terri was receiving care, disconnected the feeding tube on March 18, 2005, and she died on March 31, 2005. In all, the Schiavo case involved 14 appeals and numerous motions, petitions, and hearings in the Florida courts; five suits in federal district court; Florida legislation struck down by the Supreme Court of Florida; federal legislation; and four denials of certiorari from the U.S. Supreme Court. The case also spurred highly visible activism from the pro-life movement and disability rights groups.

Today, advance directives, which are recognized in some form throughout the United States, are widely accepted not only as a way to identify preferences for life-sustaining care for use when patients have lost decision making ability, but also as a general framework for decision making near the end of life.

Public Discussion and Debate

One other milestone that has had a tremendous influence on advanced illness care occurred in 1969 with the publication of Dr. Elisabeth Kubler-Ross's international best-seller, *On Death and Dying*.[121] In this book, the author describes her now well-known and widely accepted five stages of grief and makes a plea for home care as opposed to treatment in an institutional setting. She makes the case that patients should have a choice and the ability to participate in the decisions that affect their destiny. Three years later, she testified at the first national hearings on death with dignity conducted by the U.S. Senate Special Committee on Aging. In her testimony, she said, "We live in a very particular death-denying society. We isolate both the dying and the old, and it serves a purpose. They are reminders of our own mortality. We should not institutionalize people. We can give families more help with home care and visiting nurses, giving the families and the patients the spiritual, emotional and financial help in order to facilitate the final care at home."[122]

All of these efforts to bring the issues of advanced illness care out into the open for public discussion and debate, to promote the use of hospice and advance directives, and to fundamentally reexamine how we approach death and dying and care for people with advanced illness led the National Academy of Sciences Institute of Medicine in 1997 to take a comprehensive look at the state of advanced illness care in America in a landmark report titled, *Approaching Death: Improving Care at the End of Life*.[123] The report found that much progress has been made in improving advanced illness care, especially with regard to the clinical, organizational and ethical practices of palliative medicine that are implemented through hospices, interdisciplinary care teams in varied settings; development of innovative educational programs; and implementation of effective measurement, quality monitoring and improvement strategies.

Nevertheless, the report also identified four broad deficiencies that must be addressed to improve advanced illness care:

1. Too many people suffer needlessly at the end of life, both from errors of omissions (when caregivers fail to provide palliative and supportive care known to be effective) and from errors of commission (when caregivers pursue aggressive treatments that are known to be ineffective or even harmful and may prolong or even dishonor the period of dying).

2. Legal, organizational and economic obstacles conspire to obstruct reliably excellent care at the end of life. For example, fragmented organizational structures often complicate coordination and continuity of care and impede further development and use of palliative care strategies.

3. The education and training of physicians and other health care professionals fail to provide them with the proper attitudes, knowledge and skills required to care well for a dying patient.

4. Current knowledge and understanding are insufficient to guide and support the consistent practice of evidence-based medicine at the end of life. Biomedical and clinical research have focused almost exclusively on developing knowledge that contributes to the prevention, detection or cure of disease and to prolonging life. Research on the end stages of diseases and the physiological bases of symptom relief has had negligible support.

More generally, the report concluded that people have not yet discovered how to talk realistically, but comfortably about the end of life—nor have they learned how to value the period of dying as it is now experienced by most people.[124]

Given these deficiencies, the report went on to offer seven recommendations for improving advanced illness care.

1. People with advanced, potentially fatal illnesses and those close to them should be able to expect and receive reliable, skillful and supportive care.

2. Physicians, nurses, social workers and other health professionals must

commit themselves to improving care for dying patients and to using existing knowledge effectively to prevent and relieve pain and other symptoms.

3. Because many problems in care stem from system problems, policymakers, consumer groups and purchasers of health care should work with health care practitioners, organization and researchers to strengthen methods for measuring the quality of life and other outcomes for dying patients and those close to them; develop better tools and strategies for improving the quality of care and holding health care organizations accountable for care at the end of life; revise mechanisms for financing care so that they encourage rather than impede good end-of-life care and sustain rather than frustrate coordinated systems of excellent care; and reform drug prescription laws, burdensome regulations, and state medical board policies and practices that impede effective use of opiods to relieve pain and suffering.

4. Educators and other health professionals should initiate changes in undergraduate, graduate and continuing education to ensure that practitioners have relevant attitudes, knowledge and skills to care well for dying patients.

5. Palliative care should become, if not a medical specialty, at least a defined area of expertise, education and research.

6. The nation's research establishment should define and implement priorities for strengthening the knowledge base for end-of-life care.

7. A continuing public discussion is essential to develop a better understanding of the modern experience of dying, the options available to patients and families and the obligations of communities to those approaching death.[125]

The IOM's comprehensive analysis contained in *Approaching Death: Improving Care at the End of Life* spurned a number of significant efforts to improve advanced illness care in America. One of the most significant was the Robert Wood Johnson Foundation's *Last Acts* campaign for improving end-of-life care that began in 1995 and ended in 2005. *Last Acts* was a national communications campaign that was part of RWJF's *Targeted End-of-Life Projects Initiative*, which supports projects to improve care at the end of life. As a coalition of more than 800 national health and consumer groups, Last Acts worked to improve communication and decision making for consumers about their own death, change the culture of health care institutions and change American culture and attitudes toward death and dying. *Last Acts* established task forces to develop plans, and hired communications agencies to manage processes of the task forces and work with the public and policy audiences. Among its long list of successes, *Last Acts* developed the first-ever state-by-state report card that rated each state on eight key indices of the availability and quality of end-of-life care.[126] The campaign also made some important progress in raising professional awareness of end-of-life care issues. Coalition members viewed *Last Acts* as an important information resource on related issues and benefited from the campaign by feeling part of a larger community and receiving important support to do their work on the local level.

Despite its many successes, *Last Acts* faced several challenges. An evaluation found that the campaign did not have a visible public presence and was perceived to benefit primarily the coalition partners, being somewhat distanced from the public, the primary target audience. In addition, there was no specific evaluation of how *Last Acts* affected AD/ACP behavior.[127]

Another significant effort was *The Missoula Demonstration Project*, established in 1996 to better understand the experience of dying and to demonstrate the value of a community-based approach to medical and psychosocial support to improve the quality of life for dying patients. This project began with a series of studies to get a better sense of the needs of the community, both patients and providers. This "community profile" characterized, among others, how people die in Missoula, how they view death and dying, how people experience medical and social care at the end of life, and how people in Missoula care for and support one another during dying and grief. The project convened a number of task forces comprised of providers and lay community members to determine the types of interventions to be implemented, guided by the community profile. In addition to other data collection efforts by the task forces, the profile enabled a segmented and targeted approach to behavior change around advance directives, advanced care planning, and end-of-life care more generally.[128]

An example of a statewide social marketing campaign to improve end-of-life care is "Kokua Mau" (Hawaiian for "continuous care"). This was a community-state partnership funded by the Robert Wood Johnson Foundation, other foundations, the State of Hawaii, health care provider organizations, and insurance companies. The behavior change approach of Kokua Mau involved numerous tactics targeted to different populations: health care providers, faith communities, policy makers, and the general public. These efforts included: policy analysis and communication of policy recommendations to key policy makers, development of new courses for health care professionals, training in various settings of care, training in faith communities and supporting churches to expand outreach programs, maintaining a speakers' bureau, and producing informational materials to be disseminated widely across the state.

An evaluation published in 2005 found that dissemination of campaign materials stimulated growth of community coalitions to serve different communities and target populations. The campaign reached over 17,000 people through direct education efforts and almost 850,000 through print, radio, television, and electronic public service announcements and stories. Between 1998 and 2000, advance directive completion rates increased modestly (from 29% to 32%). In addition, hospice admissions increased substantially (by 20% between 1999 and 2001), but the proportion of the population dying in a hospital did not change.[129]

An example focused specifically on advance directives education is the *Respecting Choices* program, which was first implemented community-wide in La Crosse, Wisconsin in 2004 and have since been implemented in other populations, including the chronically ill community-dwelling elderly. The program took several approaches to effect change that since has been integrated as the routine standard of care across the community in La Crosse. These include: training and continuing education for local advance directive educators; placement of advance directive educators at all health care organizations; standard policies and practices for documenting, maintaining, and using advance directives; and community-wide education through wide dissemination of educational materials. All of the patient education materials developed for *Respecting Choices* were developed locally, with input from the target audiences.

An evaluation conducted two years after the implementation of *Respecting Choices* found that 85% of eligible patients had completed an advance directive and treatment matched the patients' wishes as stated in the advance directive for 98% of all deaths. A baseline community-wide survey revealed that about 15% of the population had a completed advance directive prior to the implementation of Respecting Choices. Although the populations are not directly comparable, the findings from the formal evaluation suggest that this program had an important influence on improving completion and implementation of advance directives.[130]

This is by no means a comprehensive list of the efforts that have been initiated nationwide to improve advanced illness care in America. It does however, offer a glimpse into the kinds of efforts that organizations and communities have undertaken and the impact they have had and are having.

In a follow up to its 1997 report, the Institute of Medicine released a new report, *Dying in America: Improving Quality and Honoring Individual Preferences Near the End of Life*, in September 2014.[131] Based upon the progress that has been made, the report concludes that "a patient-centered, family-oriented approach to care near the end of life should be a high national priority and that compassionate, affordable, and effective care for these patients is an achievable goal."[132]

ENDNOTES

Notes for Chapter 1

1   Nancy Brown, CEO American Heart Association. Summary Report of the National Summit on Advanced Illness Care, Coalition to Transform Advanced Care (C-TAC), Washington, DC., , January 29-30, 2013.

2   Donna L. Hoyert, Ph.D., and Jiaquan Xu, M.D., Division of Vital Statistics, "Deaths: Preliminary Data for 2011," Centers for Disease Control and Prevention, http://www.cdc.gov/nchs/data/nvsr/nvsr61/nvsr61_06.pdf.

3   U.S. Department of Health and Human Services. *Multiple Chronic Conditions—A Strategic Framework: Optimum Health and Quality of Life for Individuals with Multiple Chronic Conditions.* Washington, DC. December 2010. http://www.hhs.gov/ash/initiatives/mcc/mcc_framework.pdf.

4   Lichter, Allen S., MD,. CEO, American Society of Clinical Oncology. Summary Report of the National Summit on Advanced Illness Care, Coalition to Transform Advanced Care (C-TAC), Washington, DC., January 29-30, 2013.

5   Institute of Medicine of the National Academies. *Dying in America: Improving Quality and Honoring Individual Preferences Near the End of Life.* The National Academies Press, Washington, DC, September 2014.

6   See Hammes, Bernard J., Ph.D. *Having Your Own Say: Getting the Right Care When it Matters Most,* Washington, DC: CHT Press, 2012.

7   ReAct: Respect a Caregiver's Time: http://reactconnection.com/

8   Bodenheimer, T. 2008. "Coordinating Care — A Perilous Journey through the Health Care System," in . New England Journal of Medicine 358 (March 6): 1064-1071.

9   Krakauer, R., Spettell, C.M., Reisman, L. and Wade, M.J. "Opportunities to Improve The Quality of Care For Advanced Illness," Health Affairs 28(5) (2009):

1357-1359; Spettell, C.M., Rawlins, W.S., Krakauer, R., Fernandes, J., Breton, M.E.S., Gowdy, W., . . . Brennan, T.A. 2009." A Comprehensive Case Management Program To Improve Palliative Care," Journal of Palliative Medicine 12(9) (2009): 827-832.

10 An analysis of data from this project is near publication, according to Jeff Burnich.

11 McCarthy, D, Johnson, MB, and Audet, A-M. "Recasting Rreadmissions By Placing The Hospital Role In Community Context," JAMA 309(4) (2013): 351-352.

12 King, Dr. Martin Luther, Jr. Strength to Love. New York: Harper's, (1963).

13 La Montague, Christina., "Medical Bills Are the Biggest Cause of U.S. Bankruptcies." Reported by Dan Mangan, CNBC, June 25, 2013. Accessed at http://www.cnbc.com/id/100840148.

Notes for Chapter 2

14 National Hospice and Palliative Care Organization. Hospice Care in America, 2012 edition. http://www.nhpco.org/sites/default/files/public/Statistics_Research/2012_Facts_Figures.pdf.

15 Donald M. Berwick, MD. "What 'Patient-Centered' Should Mean: Confessions of an Extremist," Health Affairs Vol. 28, no. 4 (July/August 2009): 555-565. Available online at Health Affairs Web Exclusive 555 DOI 10.1377/hlthaff.28.4.w555 ©2009 Project HOPE–The People-to-People Health Foundation, Inc.

16 Atul Gawande. "Letting Go: What Should Medicine Do When It Can't Save Your Life?" The New Yorker, August 2, 2010. Available online at www.newyorker.com/reporting/2010/08/02/100802fa_fact_gawande.

17 Michael Wolf. "A Life Worth Ending," New York Magazine, May 28, 2012. Available online at http://nymag.com/news/features/parent-health-care-2012-5/.

18 Charles Ornstein. "How Mom's Death Changed My Views on End of Life

Care," Washington Post, February 28, 2013. Available online at http://www.propublica.org/article/how-moms-death-changed-my-thinking-about-end-of-life-care.

19   See The Conversation Project at http://theconversationproject.org/.

20   See Honoring Choices at http://www.honoringchoices.org/.

21   See the Video at http://www.pbs.org/wgbh/pages/frontline/facing-death/.

22   C-TAC Research Brief. "Public Perceptions of Advanced Illness Care: How Can We Talk When There's No Shared Language," Washington, DC: Coalition to Transform Advanced Care, 2011, updated Feb. 2014.

23   Ibid.

24   Field, Marilyn J. and Cassel, Christine, K., Editors. "Approaching Death: Improving Care at the End of Life," National Academy of Sciences, Institute of Medicine, Division of Health Care Services, Washington, DC: National Academy Press (1997).

25   Singer PA, Martin DK, and Kelner M. "Quality end-of-life care: patients' perspectives," JAMA 281(2) (January 13, 1999): 163-8.

26   Steinhauser KE1, Christakis NA, Clipp EC, McNeilly M, McIntyre L, and Tulsky JA. "Factors considered important at the end of life by patients, family, physicians, and other care providers," JAMA 284(19) (November 15, 2000): 2476-82.

27   Institute of Medicine of the National Academies. "Dying in America: Improving Quality and Honoring Individual Preferences Near the End of Life." Washington, DC: The National Academies Press, September, 2014.

28   Erik K. Fromme, MD, MCR, Dana Zive, MPH, Terri A. Schmidt, MD, MS, Jeffifer N.B. Cook, BA, GCPH, and Susan W. Tolle, MD. "Association Between Physician Orders for Life-Sustaining Treatment for Scope of Treatment and In-Hospital Death in Oregon." JAGS 62 (2014):1246-1251.
Hern, HE Jr., Koenig BA, Moore LJ, and Marshall PA. "The Difference That Culture Can Make in End-of-Life Decision-making." Cambridge Quarterly of Healthcare Ethics 7 (1998): 27-40.

Notes for Chapter 3

29 Hern, HE Jr., Koenig BA, Moore LJ, and Marshall PA. "The Difference That Culture Can Make in End-of-Life Decision-making." Cambridge Quarterly of Healthcare Ethics 7 (1998): 27-40.

30 Ibid.

31 Donald Friedman, MD. "Hope In The Midst of Illness," available online at www.jewishsacredaging.com. August 29, 2011.

32 Rabbi Richard F, Address, D.Min. "Medicine: A Partnership of Trust and Faith," www.bmj.com. February 17, 2014.

33 Views on End-of-Life Medical Treatments, Pew Research Center Religion & Public Life Project, November 21, 2013. Available online at http://www.pewforum.org/2013/11/21/views-on-end-of-life-medical-treatments.

34 Op. Cit., Pew Research Center Report, p. 6.

35 Dr. Kenneth Pargament. "When God Goes To Therapy," Spirituality and Health (May/June 2014): 26.

36 Abraham Joshua Heschel. "The Patient as a Person," Speech before the American Medical Association, June 1964, reprinted in The Insecurity of Freedom, 33. New York, NY: Schocken Books, 1972.

Notes for Chapter 4

37 MetLife Mature Market Institute, National Alliance for Caregiving, University of Pittsburgh. "The MetLife study of working caregivers and employer health care costs." February 2010.

38 "It's about how you live at work: an employer's guide to work-life programs and policies." Caring Connections. Alexandria, Va.: National Hospice and Palliative Care Organization: 2007.

39 AARP. Staying Ahead of the Curve 2013: AARP Multicultural Work and Career Study, Perceptions of Age Discrimination in the Workplace—Ages 45-74. Washington, DC: AARP 2013.

40 Cinko, Andrew, McDonough, Michael and Schlisserman, Courtney. Workers Over 65 Vie With Teens in Labor Market for First Time Since Truman, Bloomberg News, July 13, 2010. Accessed at http://www.bloomberg.com/insight/teens.html

41 Op. Cit., AARP.

42 MetLIfe Mature Market Institute; National Alliance for Caregiving. The MetLife caregiving cost study: productivity losses to U.S. business 2006. http://www.caregiving.org/data/Caregiver%20Cost%20Study.pdf. Accessed February 17, 2014.

43 National Alliance for Caregiving; AARP. Caregiving in the U.S. 2009. Available at: http://assets.aarp.org/rgcenter/il/caregiving_09_fr.pdf. Accessed February 17, 2014.

44 National Alliance for Caregiving; AARP. Caregiving in the U.S. 2009. Available at: http://assets.aarp.org/rgcenter/il/caregiving_09_fr.pdf. Accessed February 17, 2014.

45 Cochrane JJ, Goering PN, and Rogers JM. "The mental health of informal caregivers in Ontario: an epidemiological survey," American Journal of Pubic Health 87 (1997): 2002-2007.

46 Cannuscio CC, Jones C, Kawachi I, Colditz GA, Berkman L., and Rimm E. "Reverberation of family illness: a longitudinal assessment of informal caregiver and mental health status in the nurses' health study," American Journal of Public Health 92 (2009): 1305-1311.

47 MetLife Mature Market Institute, National Alliance for Caregiving, University of Pittsburgh. "The MetLife study of working caregivers and employer health care costs." February 2010.

48 MetLife Mature Market Institute. The MetLife caregiving cost study: productivity losses to U.S. business. www.maturemarketinstitute.com.

49   Ibid.

50   Lynn Feinberg, Susan C. Reinhard, Ari Houser, and Rita Choula. "Valuing the Invaluable: 2011 Update - The Growing Contributions and Costs of Family Caregiving," AARP Public Policy Institute, July 2011.

51   MetLife Mature Market Institute; National Alliance for Caregiving. "The MetLife caregiving cost study: productivity losses to U.S. business 2006." http://www.caregiving.org/data/Caregiver%20Cost%20Study.pdf. Accessed February 19, 2014.

52   "Impact of Advanced Illness on the Workplace: What Employers Need to Know; Communicating with Target Audiences in the Workplace," National Business Group on Health; 2010

53   Brumley RD, Enguidanos S, and Cherin DA. "Effectiveness of a home-based palliative care program for end-of-life," Journal of Palliative Medicine 6 (5) (2003): 715-24.

Notes for Chapter 5

54   Examples include: Aetna's Compassionate Care™ program, Sutter Health's Advanced Illness Management (AIM)™ program, Gundersen Health System's Respecting Choices® program and others discussed throughout this chapter.

55   Hammes BJ and Briggs LA. "Respecting Choices: Building a Systems Approach to Advance Care

56   Planning." La Crosse, WI: Gundersen Lutheran Medical Foundation; 2012.

57   Hammes BJ. Having Your Own Say: Getting the Right Care When It Matters Most. Washington, DC: CHT Press, 2012.

58   Minnesota Public Radio, "Twin Cities program helps patients discuss end of life planning." http://www.allinanews.com/2011/06/allina-program-helps-patients-discuss-end-of-life-planning.

59   Unpublished data from UnitedHealth Group.

60 R. D. Della Penna, J. B. Engelhardt, V. M. Rizzo et al. "Effectiveness of care coordination and health counseling in advancing illness," The American Journal of Managed Care 15(11) (2009): 817-825.

61 J. D. Rockoff, "Palliative Care Gains Favor as It Lowers Costs," Wall Street Journal, February 23, 2014. Accessed at http://online.wsj.com/news/articles/SB10001424052702303942404579363050214972722.

62 U.S. Senate, Special Committee on Aging. Written Testimony. Hearing, May 21st, 2014. Available at: https://www.ahip.org/ACPVisionAIllnessCare5212014.

63 The goal here is similar to that described as part of the Institute of Medicine's work to develop a standardized model for evaluating return on investment for electronic health records implementation. See e.g.,http://healthaffairs.org/blog/2014/01/06/a-standard-model-for-evaluating-return-on-investment-from-electronic-health-record-implementation/.

Notes for Chapter 6

64 C-TAC. "C-TAC Launches its Policy Maker Story Initiative." February 6th, 2014. www.thectac.org.

65 Center for Bioethics. "State of Palliative Care: What can we do together?" Senator Mark Warner (D-VA). https://www.youtube.com/watch?v=U_xxp2jB3dU&feature=share&list=PLBH551bY2k3SQYF-b9iKJvNuemuZm0JEV&index=1.

66 B. Guy Peters. American Public Policy: Promise and Performance (9th ed.), 4. Thousand Oaks, California: CQ Press, 2013.

67 NHPCO. "History of Hospice Care." http://www.nhpco.org/history-hospice-care.

68 House, Patient Self Determination Act of 1990, 101st Congress. HR 4449; available from THOMAS Library of Congress.

69 House, Medicare Prescription Drug and Modernization Act of 2003. 108th Congress. HR 1; available from THOMAS Library of Congress.

70 Pear, Robert. "Obama Returns to End-of-Life Plan that Caused Stir," The New York Times, December 25th, 2010. http://www.nytimes.com/2010/12/26/us/politics/26death.html?pagewanted=all&_r=0.

71 C-TAC. Advanced Illness Policy Review: The Landscape for Improving Advanced Illness Care in America. November 2013.

72 Bipartisan, Bicameral Effort Underway to Advance Medicare Post-Acute Reform. Committee on Ways & Means. http://waysandmeans.house.gov/news/documentsingle.aspx?DocumentID=373213.

73 C-TAC. Policy Framework. http://advancedcarecoalition.org/wp-content/uploads/2011/10/Policy-Framework.pdf

74 C-TAC has created a Policy Agenda for legislative and regulatory reform.

75 See e.g.,"Dignity-Driven Decision-Making," Health Affairs vol. 31 no. 6 (June 2012): 1269-1276

76 See e.g., House, Personalize Your Care Act, 113th Congress. HR 1173; available from THOMAS Library of Congress.

77 See e.g., Senate, Advance Planning and Compassionate Care Act, 111th Congress. S 1150; available from THOMAS Library of Congress. House, Advance Directive Promotion Act, 111th Congress. HR 3253. Available from THOMAS Library of Congress.

78 CMS. "Advance Directives and Advance Care Planning: Legal and Policy Issues." http://aspe.hhs.gov/daltcp/reports/2007/adacplpi.htm#paradigm.

79 See e.g., American Bar Association Commission on Law and Aging, "Giving Someone a Power of Attorney for your Health Care: A Guide with an Easy-to-Use, Legal Form for All Adults" (2011), a multi-state health care power attorney form, meeting statutory requirement in all states except Indiana, Ohio, New Hampshire, Texas, and Wisconsin. http://www.americanbar.org/content/dam/aba/uncategorized/2011/2011_aging_hcdec_univhcpaform_4_2012_v2.authcheckdam.pdf.

80 Senate Special Committee on Aging. "The Sandwich Generation Squeeze: Confronting the Middle Class Struggle to Raise Kids, Care for Aging Parents, and Scrape Together Enough for Retirement in Today's Economy," June 30th, 2014.

81   See e.g., Senate, Older Americans Act Amendments. 113th Congress. S 1028. Available from THOMAS Library of Congress. Senate, Strengthening Services for America's Seniors Act. 112th Congress. S 1819. Available from THOMAS Library of Congress.

82   See e.g., Senate, Americans Giving Care to Elders (AGE) Act. 112th Congress. S. 3226. Available from THOMAS Library of Congress.

83   Connor, SR, et al. "Comparing Hospice and Nonhospice Patient Survival Among Patients Who Die Within a Three Year Window," Journal of Pain Symptom Management 33 (2007): 238-246.

84   CMMI. "Hospice Medicare Care Choices Model." Available at: http://innovation.cms.gov/initiatives/Medicare-Care-Choices/

85   CMMI. "Comprehensive End Stage Renal Disease (ESRD) Care Initiative." Available at: http://innovation.cms.gov/initiatives/comprehensive-esrd-care/.

86   CA.gov. "Dual Eligibles Coordinated Care Demonstration-CalMediConnect." Available at: http://www.dhcs.ca.gov/pages/dualsdemonstration.aspx.

87   CMMI. "Medicare Coordinated Care Demo." Available at: http://innovation.cms.gov/initiatives/Medicare-Coordinated-Care/.

88   CMMI. "Independence at Home Demonstration Project." Available at: http://innovation.cms.gov/initiatives/independence-at-home/.

89   CMS. "Medicare Acute Care Episode (ACE) Demonstration." Available at: http://www.cms.gov/Medicare/Demonstration-Projects/DemoProjectsEvalRpts/Medicare-Demonstrations-Items/CMS1204388.html.

90   National Quality Forum. "Palliative Care and End-of-Life Care," Available at http://www.qualityforum.org/Topics/Palliative_Care_and_End-of-Life_Care.aspx

91   Sen. Whitehouse (D-RI) is another important supporter for the cause and is currently developing a state-wide pilot project to transform advanced care delivery in Rhode Island. This initiative encompasses a collaboration of local community and faith-based groups in order to pinpoint gaps and needs in advanced care delivery in the state. C-TAC will play a role in the development of the state policy agenda."

92 Medicaid.gov.   "Waivers"   http://www.medicaid.gov/Medicaid-CHIP-Program-Information/By-Topics/Waivers/Waivers.html.

Notes for Chapter 7

93 Meier, Diane, MD, Director, Center to Advance Palliative Care. Summary Report of the National Summit on Advanced Illness Care, Coalition to Transform Advanced Care (C-TAC), Washington, DC, January 29-30, 2013.

94 Kelly, A., McGarry, K., Fahle, S., Marshall, S., Du, Q., and Skinner, J. (2012). "Out-of-Pocket Spending in the Last Five Years of Life," Journal of General Internal Medicine 1-6. doi: 10.1007/s11606-012-2199.

95 Institute of Medicine of the National Academies. Dying in America: Improving Quality and Honoring Individual Preferences Near the End of Life. Washington, DC: The National Academies Press, September, 2014, p. S-12.

96 McCarthy, D, Johnson, MB, and Audet, A-M. "Recasting Readmissions By Placing the Hospital Role in Community Context," JAMA. 309(4) (2013): 351-352.

97 Sudore, RL and Fried, TR. "Redefining the 'Planning' in Advance Care Planning: Preparing for End-of-Life Decision Making," Annals of Internal Medicine 153(4) (2010): 256 -261. Nicholas L., Langa K., Iwashyna T., and Weir D. "Regional Variation in the Association Between Advance Directives and End-of-Life Medicare Expenditure," JAMA 306(13) (2011): 1447-1453. Tulsky JA. "Beyond Advance Directives: Importance of Communication Skills at the End of Life," JAMA 294 (3) (2005).

98 Solomon, M.Z., Browning, D.M., Dokken, D.L., Merriman, M.P., and Rushton, C.H. "Learning that Leads to Action: Impact and Characteristics of a Professional Education Approach to Improve the Care of Critically Ill Children and Their Families," Archives of Pediatric Adolescent Medicine 164(4) (April 2010): 315-22.

99 2011 Public Opinion Research on Palliative Care. Center to Advance Palliative Care and American Cancer Society Action Network.

100 C-TAC Research Brief. "Public Perceptions of Advanced Illness Care: How Can We Talk When There's No Shared Language," Washington, DC: Coalition to Transform Advanced Care, 2011, updated Feb. 2014.

101 Sofaer S, Hopper SS, Firminger K, Naierman N, and Nelson M. "Addressing the need for public reporting of comparative hospice quality: a focus group study," The Joint Commission Journal on Quality and Public Safety 35(8) (2009): 422-429.

102 These principles are best embodied in the Plan-Do-Check-Act (PDCA) continuous cycle of performance improvement popularized by W. Edwards Deming. PDCA has been widely embraced in various forms by a wide range of industries including health care. For more information, see The W. Edwards Deming Institute, 2014, "The PDSA Cycle" at https://www.deming.org/theman/theories/pdsacycle.

103 Centers for Medicare and Medicaid Services. 2014. "Hospital Compare." Accessed September 9, 2014. http://www.medicare.gov/hospitalcompare/search.html?AspxAutoDetectCookieSupport=1.

104 Centers for Medicare and Medicaid Services. 2014. "Physician Quality Reporting System." Accessed September 9, 2014. http://www.cms.gov/Medicare/Quality-Initiatives-Patient-Assessment-Instruments/PQRS/index.html?redirect=/PQRS/.

105 Institute for Healthcare Improvement. "The IHI Triple Aim." Accessed September 9, 2014. http://www.ihi.org/Engage/Initiatives/TripleAim/pages/default.aspx

106 Health Affairs. 2012. "Reducing Waste in Health Care." Accessed September 9, 2014. http://www.healthaffairs.org/healthpolicybriefs/brief.php?brief_id=82

107 Jennifer S. Temel, MD, Joseph A. Greer, Ph.D., Alona Muzikansky, M.A., Emily R. Gallagher, R.N., Sonal Admane, M.B., B.S., M.P.H., Vicki A. Jackson, M.D., M.P.H., Constance M. Dahlin, A.P.N., Craig D. Blinderman, MD, Juliet Jacobsen, M.D., William F. Pirl, M.D., M.P.H., J. Andrew Billings, M.D., and Thomas J. Lynch, MD. "Early Palliative Care for Patients with Metastatic Non–Small-Cell Lung Cancer."New England Journal of Medicine 2010; 363:733-742 August 19, 2010 DOI: 10.1056/NEJMoa1000678.

108 See http://www.dartmouthatlas.org.

109 The NQF (http://www.qualityforum.org) is well respected and accepted in the nongovernmental sector for its work on improving quality throughout all of health care, its leadership in the quality movement, and its engagement of providers and performance improvement experts in the development of measures. CMS has engaged NQF as a partner in its development of a national quality initiative to improve care and care delivery across the United States.

110 National Quality Forum, Measures Application Partnership. 2014. "Finding Common Ground for Healthcare Priorities: Families of measures for assessing affordability, population health, and person- and family-centered care." Accessed September 11, 2014. file:///C:/Users/HP%20USER/Downloads/map_families_report.pdf

Notes for Chapter 8

111 Gawande, Atul, MD. Being Mortal: Medicine and What Matters at the End. Canada: Doubleday, 2014.

112 Institute of Medicine of the National Academies. Dying in America: Improving Quality and Honoring Individual Preferences Near the End of Life. Washington, DC: The National Academies Press, September 2014.

113 Ibid.

114 Ibid.

Notes for Appendix A

115 The term hospice is taken from the linguistic root of hospitality, and can be traced back to medieval times when it referred to a place of shelter and rest for weary travelers on a long journey.

116 HEW Secretary's Task Force on Hospice, U.S. Department of Health, Education, and Welfare, Washington, DC, Office of the Secretary, Dec. 1978. Available through National Technical Information Service, U.S. Department of Commerce, Issue No. 8209, Accession No. SHR-0006737.

117 National Hospice and Palliative Care Organization. Hospice Care in America, 2012 edition. http://www.nhpco.org/sites/default/files/public/Statistics_Research/2012_Facts_Figures.pdf.

118 Hecht, Maude. B., RN and Shiel, William C., MD. Advanced Medical Directives (Living Will, Power of Attorney, and Health Care Proxy), MedicineNet.com. http://www.medicinenet.com/script/main/art/asp?articlekey=7814.

119 Emanuel LL, Barry MJ, Stoeckle JD, Ettelson LM, and Emanuel EJ. "Advance directives for medical care—a case for greater use," New England Journal of Medicine 324(13) (Mar 28, 1991): 889-895.

120 Op. Cit. MedicineNet.com.

121 Kubler-Ross, Elisabeth. On Death and Dying. New York: Macmillan Company, 1969.

122 Kubler-Ross, Elisabeth. "Testimony before the U.S. Senate Special Committee on Aging Hearing on Death with Dignity," February 1973.

123 Field, Marilyn J. and Cassel, Christine, K., Editors. Approaching Death: Improving Care at the End of Life, National Academy of Sciences, Institute of Medicine, Division of Health Care Services, Washington, DC: National Academy Press (1997).

124 Ibid. pp. 5-7.

125 Ibid. pp. 7-12.

126 Karani R and Meier DE. "Results from the Last Acts campaign: how can we improve?" Journal of Support Oncology.1(1) (May-June 2003): 69-72.

127 Balch Associates. "Assessment of Last Acts Program Provides Recommendations for Future Direction." http://www.rwjf.org/reports/grr/038049.htm.

128 Byock I, Norris K, Curtis JR, and Patrick DL. "Improving end-of-life experience and care in the community: a conceptual framework," Journal of Pain Symptom Management 22(3) (September 2001): 759-772.

129 Braun KL, Zir A, Crocker J, and Seely MR. "Kokua Mau: a statewide effort to improve end-of-life care," Journal of Palliative Medicine 8(2) (April 2005): 313-323.

130 Feder S, Matheny RL, Loveless RS, Jr., and Rea TD. "Withholding resuscitation: a new approach to prehospital end-of-life decisions," Ann Intern Medicine 144(9) (May 2, 2006): 634-640.

131 Institute of Medicine of the National Academies. "Dying in America: Improving Quality and Honoring Individual Preferences Near the End of Life." Washington, DC: The National Academies Press, September 2014.

132 Ibid. Preface.

CPSIA information can be obtained at www.ICGtesting.com
Printed in the USA
BVOW06s0311081015

421504BV00004B/5/P

9 781320 561747